Vincent Lamont
Skyman

Vincent Young
Skyman

A Lizard to Start With

Theodore Clymer
Donald J. Bissett

Consultants

William E. Blanton EVALUATION

Milton D. Jacobson READABILITY

Ken Johnson LANGUAGE

Roger W. Shuy LINGUISTICS

E. Paul Torrance CREATIVITY

READING 720 READING 720
READING 720 READING 720
GINN
READING 720 READING 720
READING 720 READING 720

GINN AND COMPANY
A Xerox Education Company

Acknowledgments

Grateful acknowledgment is made to the following publishers, authors, and agents for permission to use and adapt copyrighted materials:

The Bobbs-Merrill Company, Inc., for "An Army in Pigtails" abridged from *An Army in Pigtails* by Harriet Evatt, copyright © 1962 by The Bobbs-Merrill Company, Inc., reprinted by permission of the publisher.

Coward, McCann & Geoghegan, Inc., for "Pilgrim Thanksgiving." Adaptation by permission of Coward, McCann & Geoghegan, Inc. from *Pilgrim Thanksgiving* by Wilma Pitchford Hays. Copyright © 1955 by Wilma Pitchford Hays.

Delacorte Press for "Something Strange Is Going On." Published as and an adaptation of *Something Queer Is Going On* by Elizabeth Levy. Copyright © 1973 by Elizabeth Levy. Reprinted with permission of Delacorte Press.

Doubleday & Company, Inc., for the poem "Mimi's Fingers" from *Fingers Are Always Bringing Me News* copyright © 1969 by Mary O'Neill. Reprinted by permission of Doubleday & Company, Inc.

Follett Publishing Company for "How Engines Talk," adapted from *How Engines Talk* by David Robert Burleigh, copyright © 1961 by Follett Publishing Company. Used by permission.

Harcourt Brace Jovanovich, Inc., for "Hai Yin, the Dragon Girl." The text of *Hai Yin, the Dragon Girl* by Joy Anderson is reproduced by permission of Harcourt Brace Jovanovich, Inc. from the volume *Hai Yin, the Dragon Girl,* illustrated by Jay Yang, © 1970 by Joy Anderson. Also for the poem beginning "Over the wintry forest . . ." from *Cricket Songs: Japanese Haiku,* translated and © 1964 by Harry Behn. Reprinted by permission of Harcourt Brace Jovanovich, Inc.

Holt, Rinehart and Winston, Inc., for the adaptation of "A Language Everyone Knows" from *A Book to Begin on Numbers* by Leslie Waller. Copyright © 1960 by Leslie Waller and Shannon Stirnweis. Abridged and adapted by permission of Holt, Rinehart and Winston, Inc. Also for the poems beginning "The rainbow is the fishing line . . ." and "The Wind is a man with a spade . . ." both from *The Sun is a Golden Earring* by Natalia Belting. Copyright © 1962 by Natalia Belting. Reprinted by permission of Holt, Rinehart and Winston, Inc.

Houghton Mifflin Company for the abridgment of "Hah-nee's Secret," for the adaptation and abridgment of "The Land of Mai," and for the Epilogue, all from *Hah-nee of the Cliff*

Book of Communications by Mary E. Nelson. Copyright 1961 © by Ottenheimer Publishers, Inc. Used by permission of the publisher.

Parents' Magazine Press for "Communicating with Picture Signs and Symbols," text only adapted from *Picture Signs and Symbols* by Winifred and Cecil Lubell. Copyright © 1972 by Winifred and Cecil Lubell. Used by permission of Parents' Magazine Press.

Mark Paterson, London, for "Numerals Are In" and "Working with Numbers," adapted from *The True Book of Numbers* by Philip Carona, published by Frederick Muller Limited. Used by permission of Mark Paterson.

Rand McNally & Company for *Kathi and Hash San, The Case of Measles* by Jean Lewis, reprinted by permission of Rand McNally & Co., publishers. Copyright 1972 by Rand McNally & Co.

Scholastic Magazines, Inc., for "Communicating with Codes" from *How to Write Codes and Secret Messages* by John Peterson. Copyright © 1966 by John Peterson. Used by permission of Four Winds Press, a division of Scholastic Magazines, Inc.

Sidgwick & Jackson Ltd, London, for the poem "India" from *The Hunter and Other Poems* by W. J. Turner. Used by permission of the publisher.

Dan Storm for "Señor Coyote and Señor Fox," adapted from his book *Picture Tales from Mexico*. Copyright, 1941, by J. B. Lippincott Company. Used by permission of the author.

Frederick Warne & Co., Inc., for *Santiago* by Pura Belpré. Copyright © 1969, Pura Belpré. Used by permission of the publisher.

Franklin Watts, Inc., for "Let's Find Out About Communications," adapted from *Let's Find Out About Communications* by Valerie Pitt, copyright © 1973 by Franklin Watts, Inc., used by permission of the publisher.

Illustrations were provided by the following: Franz Altschuler (326-337); Kathy Anderson (60-81); C. Bradford Boyce (144); Jane Caminos (104-123); Louis Cary (260-281); Michael Chauncy (42-59); Guy Danella (84-101 and 124-137); Diane Dawson (284-291); Arlene Dubanovich (192-201); Bert Dodson (294-303); Len Ebert (12-27); Lois Ehlert (166-177); Randall Enos (292-293 and 324-325); Claudia Fregosi (304-305); Nahid Haghighat (316-323); Gordon Laite (204-231); Don Leake (140–151); Dora Leder (306-313); Richard Loehle (190-191); Kenneth Longtemps (30-41); Lady McCrady (102-103); Leslie Morrill (246-259); Nickzad Nodjoumi (314-315); Julie O'Neil (142, L. CR. & R.); Judy Pelikan (152-165); John Pyk (178-189); Ted Rand (338-367); Bill Sumner (142, CL); Phero Thomas (232-245). George Ulrich (368-377); Christine Westerberg (28-29).

The cover and unit introduction pages were designed by Gregory Fossella Associates.

4

Contents

Unit 1 **GROWING IS QUIET**   **10**

Izzard   LONZO ANDERSON   **12**

My Lizard *Poem*   KAYE STARBIRD   **29**

Hai Yin, the Dragon Girl   JOY ANDERSON   **30**

Santiago   PURA BELPRÉ   **42**

Annie and the Old One   MISKA MILES   **60**

My People *Poem*   BERNICE GEORGE   **80**

Unit 2 **AHA! A SLEUTH!**   **82**

Kathi and Hash San   **84**
   The Case of Measles   JEAN LEWIS

Cat *Poem*   DOROTHY BARUCH   **102**

The Case of Nellie and the Ambergris   **104**
   DONALD J. SOBOL

The Case of the Blueberry Pies   **114**
   DONALD J. SOBOL

Something Strange Is Going On   **124**
   ELIZABETH LEVY

Unit 3   SIGNS, SYMBOLS, AND CODES   **138**

Communication: Just Words?   **140**
   Let's Find Out About Communications
     VALERIE PITT
   Let's Begin at the Beginning   MARY E. NELSON
Speaking of Numbers   **152**
   A Language Everyone Knows   LESLIE WALLER
   Numerals Are In and
   Working with Numbers   PHILIP CARONA
Communicating with Picture Signs and   **166**
   Symbols   WINIFRED AND CECIL LUBELL
   Signs That Lead the Way
   Picture Signs That Tell a Story
   Flags Are Symbols Too
   Symbols Tell about Customs
Communicating with Codes   JOHN PETERSON   **178**
   Space Codes
   Hidden Words Code
   Alphabet Codes
   More Messages to Decode

6

Mimi's Fingers   *Poem*   MARY O'NEILL   190
How Engines Talk   DAVID ROBERT BURLEIGH   192

Unit 4   LONG-AGO YESTERDAYS   202

Hah-nee's Secret   MARY AND CONRAD BUFF   204
The Land of Mai   MARY AND CONRAD BUFF   218
This Dream Came True   *Play*   232
    ELIZABETH H. SECHRIST
Pilgrim Thanksgiving   WILMA PITCHFORD HAYS   246
An Army in Pigtails   HARRIET EVATT   260

Unit 5   A TOUCH OF MAGIC — A TOUCH OF WONDER   282

How Vasil Vanquished the Dragon   284
    IRINA ZHELEZNOVA
The rainbow is the fishing line . . .   293
    Poem   FROM MALAYA
Señor Coyote and Señor Fox   DAN STORM   294
Coyote   *Poem*   PATRICIA MILES MARTIN   305

The Boy Who Went to the North Wind   **306**
NORSE FOLK TALE

The Wind is a man . . . *Poem*   FROM LAPLAND   **314**

Over the wintry forest . . . *Poem*   SOSEKI   **315**

The Tiger, the Brahman, and the Jackal   **316**
INDIAN FOLK TALE

India *Poem*   W. J. TURNER   **324**

To Your Good Health   RUSSIAN FOLK TALE   **326**

BOOK-LENGTH STORY

The Case of the Elevator Duck   **338**
POLLY BERRIEN BERENDS

GLOSSARY   **368**

A Lizard to Start With

Growing
Is Quiet

In the stories you are about to read, the people grow quietly. Watch them. What happens to make them grow? What happens to you from just reading about them? Maybe you have grown too without knowing it. Quietly. It's possible.

When Izzard hatches in Jamie's
hot hand, a warm friendship
also starts to grow. Friendship
between a lizard and a boy?
Seems odd at first, even to Jamie.
But as time passes, their
friendship grows and grows—
and so do Izzard and Jamie.

12

IZZARD

I found a lizard egg, tiny and white and round. I brought it home.

I held it in my hand while I took my nap in the hammock.

Tickle-tickle.

I woke up.

Wriggle-wriggle. Something was alive in my hand.

I opened my palm. There lay two pieces of egg shell and a tiny, shiny lizard staring at me.

My father looked. "The heat of your hand made it hatch," he said.

My sister looked. "It's darling! Oh, please! Give it to me!"

"I will not," I said. "It's mine."

It started to walk. I was afraid it would run away.

But no. After a while it scampered up my arm. Its feet made the tiniest tickle I ever felt on my skin.

It looked up at me, right in my eyes!

It ran across my sleeve to my shoulder. Up my bare neck it came, and onto my chin.

"What can I give it to eat?" I wondered.

"Nothing," my father said. "It will know what to do when the time comes to eat."

"May I keep it?"

"You don't have much choice," my father said. "It thinks you are its mother."

"Its *mother*! But I'm a *boy*!"

My father laughed. "As long as it *thinks* you are its mother it will stay with you."

"All right," I said. "Then I'll *be* it."

My sister started singing, "Jamie is its mo-ther, Jamie is its mo-ther, yah-yah-yah!"

I ignored her.

I tried to study my lessons for school. I couldn't. The baby lizard was starting to eat.

It sat on my bare knee, watching, watching. A sand fly came to take a bite out of me. It was so small that I could barely see it. The baby lizard jumped and caught it.

Chew-chew-chew, just like me, and *gulp* — just like me! — it swallowed the bug.

"Isn't that wonderful?" I shouted. "He did it all by himself!"

"He?" My mother sounded doubtful. "I think it's a little girl lizard."

"Yes," my father said. "If you had a boy lizard you could see the difference. A girl lizard is smaller."

"Oh," I said. "Well! Hello, there, Izzard — my daughter, the lizard!"

Izzard was not the kind of lizard that can see in the dark. She was a daytime lizard, so when night came she tried to hide inside my shirt. I put her in the pocket of my pajama top when I went to bed.

My mother worried. "You won't roll on her?"

"Oh, no!" I said. "I'll always know she's there, even when I'm asleep."

No one said I couldn't take her to school, so I did. I soon wished I hadn't.

She sat on top of my head and jumped at flies.

She sat on my desk, snapping at whatever insects came by, even when they were too big for her. I think she was showing off.

The other children in the school could not pay attention to the teacher. They could only watch little Izzard and laugh.

"Jamie," the teacher said, "you will have to get rid of that lizard."

"I can't," I said. "I'm its mother."

That was the wrong thing to say, because everybody screamed and the teacher looked angry.

"Jamie, give it to me," she said. "I'll keep it in my desk until after school." She held out her hand.

Izzard hid inside my shirt.

The teacher stamped her foot. Izzard peeked out from under my chin at her.

She laughed. She couldn't help it, I could tell.

From then on I had to leave Izzard at home when I went to school.

As soon as I came home she would run to meet me.

One day Izzard and I saw a mongoose stalking a lizard in the yard. The lizard saw it and had no place to hide. The house was too far away on one side, and the nearest tree was not near enough.

The lizard stood still, trying to look like a piece of wood.

The mongoose was not fooled. It crouched, ready to jump. I yelled to scare it, but that didn't work; I was too far away.

The lizard was desperate. It decided to run for the tree as I ran to help.

Too late! Pounce! went the mongoose.

Crunch-gulp. That was the end of the lizard. It was awful. I shuddered. I put my hand around Izzard. I must keep her safe.

I caught the flu. I had to stay in bed. Izzard stayed with me.

The night was hot, and Izzard slept in a crack by my bed instead of in my pajama pocket.

My mother moved me to a cooler room on the other side of the house. Izzard was asleep, and my mother was so worried about me that she forgot about Izzard.

I was too sick to know that Izzard was not with me.

Izzard hunted and hunted for me. I know, because it took her two whole days to find me.

By that time my fever was getting better. My head was propped on a pillow, and suddenly Izzard's nose came up over the foot of my bed. Then her eyes came up. Then she was all there and running like mad the whole length of my bed.

I was so glad to see her that I felt better right away.

While I was getting well she stayed with me.

The more I watched her and thought about it, the more I realized that Izzard didn't know that she was a lizard. There are lizards everywhere here on St. John, in the houses and outside, but she paid no attention to any of them. She was interested only in me.

In June, while Izzard was still young, my parents took my sister and me on a long trip to New York, to visit my grandmother for the summer. Izzard was not allowed to go with me.

I worried about her. Would she forget me? Would she be able to make a living without me? Would the mongoose get her?

We came home in the fall in time for school. When we got there it was evening. Izzard was nowhere to be found. Only the night lizards, with huge eyes for seeing in the dark, were there. They were shy, and ran from me.

I felt sad and lonely when I went to bed.

In the morning, as soon as it was light, *plop!*—there was Izzard.

She danced. She jumped. She burrowed under my neck on the pillow and tickled me with her wriggling.

I knew she was trying to say, "I'm so *glad* to see you! Where *have* you been?"

Her tail had a bend in it. Something *had* happened to her—I would never know what. But was I happy that she was still alive and well!

One day when I came home from school she was nowhere in the house. It was broad daylight, so I knew she was not sleeping somewhere, hiding from me.

I went out the back door and looked. There she was, six feet up on a palm tree.

She started running down the tree to come to me.

At that instant I saw the mongoose, lurking under a big leaf nearby, waiting, waiting.

I yelled, "Izzard, NO!"

She couldn't understand. She came on.

The mongoose was like lightning. It pounced.

Izzard was even quicker. Terrified, she jumped straight up into the air.

She came down on top of the mongoose's head!

Before it knew what had happened, she was off again. Jump-jump-jump—she got to me just as I was chasing the mongoose away.

She scampered up my leg and inside my shirt. She would not come out for a whole hour.

Soon after that Izzard found out she was a lizard and not a human being.

A big male lizard came near me to catch a bug. Izzard was furious. She jumped at him.

Well, he gave her the worst battle she ever had in her life.

From that moment on, her world changed.

She stared at him, then at me.

When he left, she followed him a little way. Then she came back to look at me again.

I put out my hand to pick her up. She jumped back. She wouldn't let me touch her!

Izzard afraid of *me*? I couldn't believe it. But she was. She wouldn't stay with me anymore. She stayed with the other lizards, sleeping with them in their secret night places, and hunting for her insect food on the walls and furniture instead of on me.

I was shocked. I was hurt.

"She's a grown-up lizard now," my father explained.

My mother said, "All of a sudden you look as big as a mountain to her. Suppose a mountain should reach down to pick you up. You'd be scared stiff."

"But Jamie's her *mother*!" my sister said. Once in a while a sister really understands a person better than anybody.

"Oh," I moaned. "What can I do?"

"Nothing, dear," my mother said.

"If she doesn't want you," my father said, "you'll just have to forget about her."

"But how *can* he?" my sister asked.

I couldn't and I didn't.

Summer came again, and we went to visit my grandmother in New York as usual.

When we came back in the fall, as soon as we came into the house, *plop*! onto my leg came Izzard!

She ran up to my shoulder, but she couldn't see my eyes well enough from there.

She ran onto my hand and I raised her in front of my face. She stared into my eyes, first with one eye, then with the other, and wriggled. It was like old times.

My father said, "I think she missed you and decided to forgive you for not being a lizard."

"I think so too," my sister said. "You lucky thing."

"Isn't that nice?" my mother said.

Izzard had forgiven me, all right, but she didn't stay with me. She would visit me often, but she lived with the other lizards. Anyhow, Izzard was still my very good friend.

Guess what I found on my pillow last night when I went to bed.

A lizard egg!

Do you suppose it is Izzard's—a special present just for me?

—*Lonzo Anderson*

26

What Do You Think?

1. How would you feel if you woke up and found something alive in your hand?
2. How did Izzard show that she felt Jamie was her mother?
3. How did Jamie feel when he knew Izzard had grown up?

Taking A Closer Look

1. What words would you use to describe Izzard to a friend?
2. Why didn't Jamie want the mongoose to see Izzard?
3. After Jamie had the flu, what did he discover about Izzard?
4. What was Jamie afraid would happen at home while he was in New York?
5. How did Jamie know when Izzard had grown up?
6. What was Izzard's gift to Jamie? What made the gift so special?

My Lizard

My friends all tell me they want a pet,
And though they do, as a rule,
I find that no one has wanted yet
My lizard I call O'Toole.
O'Toole is gentle and good as gold
And perfectly nice to touch;
But when I give him to kids to hold
Nobody wants him much.

My friends all play with my dog—and poke
The worm I keep in a dish.
They think my tadpole's kind of a joke,
Being half-frog, half-fish.
They all of them chase my ladybug
And shoo my ducks in the pool.
Maybe my kitten they'll even *hug,*
But NOBODY hugs O'Toole. . . .

. . . Lizards deserve a little credit.
What's so wrong with O'Toole?
Down in his hole he spends each day
Crawling around on his gizzard,
Living his life in his quiet way,
A perfectly lovely lizard.

—Kaye Starbird

29

What makes dreams come true? Is it what other people think of you? Is it what you think of yourself? Is it luck? Or is it *all* of these? Hai Yin had to find out for herself. Perhaps as she grows and discovers the answers, you will too. And growing can be fun!

Hai Yin, the Dragon Girl

In the great gray city of Taipei,[1] on the busy street of Ho Ping,[2] lived a girl named Hai Yin.[3]

Above the Precious Lady Beauty Parlor and next door to the Won Chuan Ham[4] Works, Hai Yin lived with her mother, father, baby sister Mei Mei,[5] and big brother Wu,[6] who thought girls were not good for anything. "Girls are silly," said Wu.

"But Hai Yin is different. She was born in the Year of the Dragon," her father said proudly. "My Hai Yin is a Dragon Girl."

In Taiwan, it is said that people born in the Year of the Dragon are the luckiest in the world. To be a Dragon Girl is a very fine thing. Hai Yin liked to think about it.

One day she said to her brother, "You know, Wu, someday I am going to be famous."

Wu laughed. "And how are you going to become famous? You are just a girl."

[1] Taipei (TIGH-PAY) [2] Ho Ping (HOH PING) [3] Hai Yin (HIGH YING)
[4] Won Chuan Ham (WAHN CHAHN YAHM) [5] Mei Mei (MAY MAY)
[6] Wu (WOO)

31

"*Meo gwanshi*,[1] never mind. Dragon people are clever and wise," said Hai Yin boastfully. "I will think of something."

"You are a daydreamer," Wu said loudly. "Always imagining what great things you are going to do. You are only a daydreaming dragon!"

Hai Yin's face turned red. Was she only a daydreamer? "I will show Wu that I am not just a silly girl," she thought to herself. "I must find out how to become famous."

Hai Yin ran down the steps, through the Precious Lady Beauty Parlor, and out onto Ho Ping Street.

There she saw an old friend, Mr. L. K. Kung,[2] the fortune-teller, surrounded by his charts of faces, heads, and hands.

"Hai Yin, you are walking as the dragon flies today. What is on your mind?"

"Mr. Kung, can you tell me if I will become famous?" asked Hai Yin.

Mr. Kung examined Hai Yin's face. He measured her forehead and consulted his charts. "You have a high forehead, which means you have intelligence," he said. "And your chin is nice and round. That means you will be lucky. Perhaps," he said, smiling, "you will be famous."

"Can you tell me how?"

[1] *Meo gwanshi* (may-oh GWAHN-shee)   [2] Kung (KOONG)

"That, my little lotus seed, the charts cannot say,"
said Mr. Kung kindly. "You must find out for yourself."

Slowly now, not like the dragon flies, Hai Yin walked
along Ho Ping. She was thinking that she should not
have boasted to Wu that she was clever and wise.
"Wu was right. I am only a silly girl, a daydreaming
dragon."

For many weeks Hai Yin said nothing more to Wu
about becoming famous. But she often thought of what
Mr. Kung had said: "You must find out for yourself."
Somehow, she must think of something. But what
could a *girl* do?

One February day, Hai Yin's father hung a long string of firecrackers from the window. Crack! Snap! Pop! Bang! *Ei-yo,*[1] what a noise! Baby Mei Mei covered her ears. It was the New Year!

"My Dragon Girl will bring us all good luck this year," Hai Yin's father said happily, "because this is the Year of the Dragon!"

The Year of the Dragon! Hai Yin was excited. "Perhaps I will find a way to become famous," she thought.

Ho Ping Street was very gay. Red good luck signs lined each door. Oranges, apples, and rice cakes filled the stands. Everyone dressed in new clothes and carried gifts to relatives.

[1] *Ei-yo* (IGH-yah)

A favorite place for children was the shop of Mr. Pan,[1] the lantern man, where shiny bright, new lanterns were swinging and swaying on every side. They knew that the best part of the long New Year holiday was coming soon.

On the night of the first full moon, there was a special time for children—the Lantern Festival! On that night it was said that spirits could be seen in the sky. To help the moon shine more brightly, children pulled lighted paper lanterns through the streets. They were beautiful, like shining eyes in the dark.

Many people walked all the way to Lungshan[2] Temple, where the prettiest lanterns were hung high from the ceiling for everyone to see. There the Mayor of Taipei would give a prize to the person who made the most unusual and beautiful lantern.

[1] Pan (PAN)   [2] Lungshan (LUNG-shan)

That is why, days before the Lantern Festival, the children on Ho Ping crowded around Mr. Pan's shop, where they looked and looked at the lanterns. There were rabbits and rams, ships and stars, airplanes, flowers, and shrimps. How hard it was to choose!

Every year Hai Yin loved to watch Mr. Pan make the lanterns. Carefully he twisted the tiny bamboo pieces and tied them with wire. Sometimes she helped him paste the shiny colored paper over the top.

This year, Mr. Pan let Hai Yin make a lantern all by herself, a funny lion with a green tongue.

"You have learned very well, Hai Yin," Mr. Pan said. "You can make your own lanterns now."

And that gave Hai Yin an idea. *Ei-yo*, what a marvelous idea it was! But it must be kept a secret.

She bought bamboo, paper, and paste from Mr. Pan. Quickly she ran down the street, past the stands of bright fruit and the Won Chuan Ham Works, through the Precious Lady Beauty Parlor, and up the stairs. There, where no one could see her, Hai Yin started to work. Very carefully she bent bamboo and cut shiny paper.

Wu was curious. "What are you doing?" he asked.

"You can't see now. You must wait until the Lantern Festival."

"What a silly girl!" said Wu.

All through the New Year holiday, Hai Yin worked on her secret. The longer she worked, the grander became her plan.

The moon grew more round. The night of the Lantern Festival drew close. There was not much time left.

One night Hai Yin's mother served the special rice dumplings that meant the moon was full.

The Lantern Festival had begun!

"Hurry, Hai Yin!" her mother called. "Children are already in the street with their lanterns."

But Hai Yin could not hurry. There was still more work to do. It must be perfect.

"You will be too late for the festival," said Wu.

Hai Yin's fingers flew—twisting, bending, cutting. Now the full moon was shining in her window. At last, she pasted on the final bit of paper. Her surprise was ready.

"You can see now," she called.

Mei Mei, Wu, and their mother and father stared and stared. They could not believe their eyes.

Hai Yin was standing proudly by a lantern—but not a small, ordinary lantern like the ones in Mr. Pan's shop. Not a rabbit or a ram, a ship, a star, or a shrimp. Not anything like that!

Hai Yin's lantern stretched across the room. It had shining green and gold scales, red fiery eyes, and a waving tail!

A dragon! Hai Yin had made a dragon for the Year of the Dragon!

"*Ei-yo*!" said baby Mei Mei, jumping up and down.

"It is quite a good lantern," said Wu, "for a girl."

Everyone on Ho Ping Street ran to see Hai Yin's dragon. "Such a beautiful lantern should go to Lungshan Temple," they said.

So, pulling her twisting, turning dragon, Hai Yin led a parade of shining lanterns through the streets of Taipei.

What an exciting night! Fireworks exploded. Two tall generals on stilts marched by, playing tricks on the children. Red eyes gleamed from a dark street, and the dragon dancers swirled close to Hai Yin.

At Lungshan Temple, her dragon was lifted high and hung in the entrance, where it could be admired from every side.

Suddenly a big black car rolled up to Lungshan Temple. The Mayor of Taipei stepped out. He had come to judge the lanterns.

Slowly he walked around, stopping to examine each lantern. He looked at Hai Yin's dragon for a long time.

Everyone pushed closer. Which one would he choose? Once more he walked around inside the temple. Again he stopped at the dragon. He whispered to his councilmen. They nodded their heads.

Hai Yin held her breath. Would he choose her dragon?

"I wish to announce," said the Mayor finally, "that for the very first time, the City of Taipei is awarding the prize for the most beautiful lantern to a *girl*! To Miss Hai Yin, the Dragon Girl!"

The Mayor gave Hai Yin a scroll covered with gold seals and red ribbons and a fat red New Year envelope of prize money!

Hai Yin was famous! She was the happiest girl in the great city of Taipei as she walked home to Ho Ping Street with her mother, father, baby sister Mei Mei, and brother Wu.

Wu was the proudest of all. Never again did he call Hai Yin a daydreaming dragon.

—*Joy Anderson*

What Do You Think?

1. How did Wu feel about Hai Yin's dragon? Do you think Wu changed his attitude about his sister? Explain your answer.

2. What *might* have happened differently if Hai Yin had taken Wu's teasing seriously?

3. How did Hai Yin show from the beginning she was unusual? What made her dream come true?

Taking A Closer Look

1. Why was Hai Yin's father so sure that Hai Yin was a very special person?

2. Wu thought Hai Yin was a dreamer. What did *she* think of herself?

3. What did the fortune-teller, Mr. Kung, say about Hai Yin?

4. What gave Hai Yin the idea for making a lantern?

5. How did her lantern happen to go to Lungshan Temple?

6. What prizes did the Mayor give Hai Yin?

7. What made Hai Yin happiest of all?

Santiago and his family came to their new country with their most personal treasures. He brought tales of his special friend Selina. His mother brought stories about the beauty and culture of their homeland. Together they share their loves with Santiago's new friends. How do Santiago's classmates grow from what Santiago shows them?

42

Santiago

"Santiago!" Mother called from the kitchen.

No answer.

"Santiago Román!"[1]

Still no answer.

His mother walked into the parlor. There sat Santiago staring at the light through the stereoscope.

"I have been calling you, Santiago. Did you not hear me?"

"But I am looking at the picture of Selina grandmother sent me."

"Selina, Selina. Morning, noon and night, you speak of nothing else. You left her in Puerto Rico,[2] but to hear you talk one would think she is here in New York. Put away that stereoscope. Come, have your breakfast or you will be late for school."

---

[1] Santiago Román (sahn-tee-AH-goh roh-MAHN)
[2] Puerto Rico (PWEHR-toh REE-koh)

Santiago gave the picture one more quick look, then he put the stereoscope on the table next to a large carved gourd. Slowly, he followed his mother to the kitchen.

"May I take the stereoscope to school, Mamá?"

"Whatever gave you that idea? You know we don't allow it out of the house."

"I want the children to see Selina too."

"So you talk about that hen at school also. Finish your breakfast, Santiago, before you have more silly ideas."

Santiago's mother handed him a paper bag. "Here's your lunch. The permission slip is signed. It is a good day to eat lunch by the river," she said. But Santiago ate only a little breakfast. Then he picked up his lunch and the slip and waited for his mother to get her pocketbook.

How he wished he could take the stereoscope to school and show Selina to Ernie—especially to Ernie. Of all the children in his class, Ernie was the only one who didn't believe Selina was real. He wanted Ernie to believe about Selina.

"Let us go," said his mother.

The school was a block away, just around the corner from where they lived. They hurried to the corner, then had to wait for a green light before crossing.

"I don't see any other children going to school, Santiago. You must be quite late." The light changed and they rushed across. "Now run," his mother said and kissed him. "God be with you," she said and waved.

Santiago ran toward the main entrance. Halfway there he suddenly stopped. Was he seeing things? He closed his eyes and opened them quickly. It was true. Across the street and under a large log outside the parking lot, a hen—a large white hen—was pecking. Santiago ran on to the school. He *was* late.

When he entered his classroom, everybody was busy. "Listen everyone! I just saw a hen—a large white hen!" he cried.

Clay modeling, finger painting, block and cardboard building, all stopped at once. All of the students surrounded Santiago—all but one. Ernie, whose hands clutched tiny nails and a hammer, paid no attention.

"Where did you see a hen?" asked the children.

"Nowhere. He did not see a hen," said Ernie without looking around.

"I did so," Santiago insisted.

"Here we go again," said Miss Taylor. "I feel just like a referee, and always the subject is hens. Let Santiago finish his story, Ernie."

"You know the parking lot across the street?" continued Santiago. "Well, right there outside the wire fence is a large log. Pecking under the log is the hen."

"Oh, you only thought you saw a hen," said Ernie. "This is New York City. Hens don't walk in the streets here."

"This one does, because I just saw her."

"That's enough, Ernie," said Miss Taylor.

"Santiago, you are sure you saw this hen?"

"Yes, Miss Taylor."

"Good. Then we can settle this matter. We will go and look at this hen."

"Now, now?" asked the children.

"Now we go back to work. On our way to the river, we will stop by the parking lot."

Lucille and María went back to their finger painting. Hector and Ernie continued building their castle. Shirley and Clarice started sorting the sea-shells that were to be pasted on a sewing box. Santiago and Joseph began to cut table mats.

Miss Taylor smiled to herself as she thought that for once the children were all carefully working. That Santiago, she thought, he seems to be in two places at once. He lives in New York, but his mind is full of adventures with that pet hen back in Puerto Rico. Many times he has told the children about her. And all believe him, that is, all except Ernie. You have to show Ernie.

"There's no more paste, Miss Taylor," said Clarice. "Shall I get more?"

Miss Taylor looked at the clock. "If we are to stop by the parking lot, we had better start getting ready. Put everything aside and wash your hands."

48

Lucille and María were the first ones at the washing sink. "I don't want a lick and a promise on those hands. Wash them clean." All the children washed and scrubbed as best they could. Soon they were ready to go.

"Stay close to your partners," said Miss Taylor, and led the way. They went down into the subway station close to the school and out the opposite exit to save time. Once outside, they went past the newspaper stand, the drug store, and the Elk's hall. Ahead was the parking lot. Two workers in overalls were sitting on the log eating their lunches. The children surrounded them.

"Where is she?" asked Santiago.

"Where is who?" asked the men.

"The white hen," explained Santiago.

"Look, Sonny, this is a parking lot, not a chicken coop."

"See!" exclaimed Ernie. "I told you. You did not see a hen."

"Perhaps she is in the parking lot," suggested Santiago.

They all peered through the wire fence. They all saw cars and trucks of all sizes and colors, three large trees in the rear and a large bulldog tied to a post. But none saw a large white hen. While they were looking, another worker joined the two on the log.

"What goes on here?" he asked.

"A search for a hen. You did not see her, did you?"

"Who me? Is this a joke?"

"Let me explain," said Miss Taylor. "Come here, Santiago. This boy says that he saw a large white hen pecking under this log this morning. We have come here in order to see her and to settle an argument. But if you, who work here, haven't seen a hen . . ."

"Wait a minute," interrupted one of the workers. "We did not say that we work here. The fact is, we work down the street and come here just to eat our lunch."

"I know someone who works here," said another. "Wait just a second." He went to the corner shop and returned with another man.

"This is Angelo. Tell him your story, boy." Santiago repeated the story once more. "Did you see her, Señor Angelo?" Angelo laughed. "Sure, sure," he said, still laughing. "That was my Rosina."

"But where . . ." Santiago didn't finish his question, for just then, through a hole in the wire fence, a large white hen appeared.

"Look, Ernie," he cried. "There she is! There she is!" Santiago jumped up and down.

"Stand still," said Angelo. "Don't frighten her. Let her come to me."

Everybody stood quietly. Ernie stared and stared. Slowly, like a great actress on a stage, Rosina walked straight to Angelo. He picked her up and smoothed her feathers.

"Does she live here?" asked the children.

"No, no. She lives just across from the George Washington Bridge. Everyday I bring Bravo, my bulldog, to guard the parking lot. Rosina stays at home. But she likes Bravo and misses him. So, every now and then, I bring her to be with him. Let us go and feed Bravo, eh Rosina?" He walked into the parking lot. Bravo saw them coming and his stumpy tail quivered in greeting.

"Boy, that's a hen to beat all hens," said Ernie.

"All, except my Selina," said Santiago quickly.

"Oh, you just say so," said Ernie.

"I can prove it."

"How?" Ernie wanted to know.

Santiago did not answer. Instead he turned to Miss Taylor. "Please come to my home for a little while. It is just down the street. I want everyone to see my Selina."

"Your Selina? I thought she was in Puerto Rico." Miss Taylor was puzzled.

"When did she fly in from Puerto Rico?" taunted Ernie. Santiago ignored him. "Please, Miss Taylor," he pleaded.

"Well, it is unusual," she said. But something in Santiago's voice made her change her mind. Was there something else besides Selina on Santiago's mind?

"All right, let us go," she said.

Santiago led the way to his home and rang the bell. His mother had never seen so many children in her home before. But if she was upset, Santiago certainly was not. Calmly he said, "This is my mother, Señora Román. My father is not here. He is working." Then he turned to his mother. "Mamá, they have come to look at Selina."

Everyone stood waiting for a hen to appear. Santiago took the stereoscope from the table and looked through to be sure the picture was straight.

"Now you all can see my Selina. Here she is!"

"How can she be in there? What is *that*?" asked Ernie ahead of everyone. Ernie always asked things first.

"A stereoscope," answered Santiago.

"A stereo what?" asked Ernie.

"Oh, something you use to look at the pictures."

"Moving pictures?" asked the children.

"No, just pictures, like the one there now."

"Let me see! Let me see!" cried the children.

Miss Taylor clapped her hands. "You are not in a playground. This is Santiago's home. Remember, we are his guests."

"Oh, it's all right," said Santiago's mother.

"Only one person can look at the stereoscope at a time," said Miss Taylor.

"Make a line."

Santiago passed the stereoscope to Lucille who was first. "I can see all of her. She is so colorful."

"Don't take all day. It's my turn now," said Horace. Lucille passed him the stereoscope.

"My, what a hen!" he cried. "All the colors of the rainbow."

And so the stereoscope was passed from hand to hand until it got to Ernie at the end of the line. Santiago held his breath. What would Ernie say? Santiago's face showed his worry. Miss Taylor noticed him. So this is the problem. Ernie. She should have guessed. This was the real reason for their visit. All of a sudden, she too became worried about what Ernie would say.

Ernie fixed the stereoscope to his eyes. He looked quietly for a while. He moved the stereoscope ever so slowly, back and forth. "Boy, this is the queen of all queens. When you move the stereo — stereoscope slowly, the hen seems to be moving. Gee, Santiago, I wish she was really here. We could put her in the parking lot with Rosina. Say, 'Rosina' and 'Selina.' Their names sound alike."

Everybody laughed. But no one laughed more than Santiago.

"Now that *you* have approved of Selina," said Miss Taylor, "what about me? I too would like to see her. Heaven knows that I have listened to enough about her."

Slowly, Ernie passed her the stereoscope. She took one look.

"Why, she is beautiful!" she exclaimed. "You are right, Ernie, she is a queen. If I had a pet hen like this, Santiago, no one could keep me from talking about her."

Santiago beamed. Miss Taylor put the stereoscope on the table. It was then that she noticed the large carved gourd. "This is a work of art," she said almost to herself. But Santiago's mother heard her and joined her at the table.

"It's very old. Like the stereoscope, it has been in our family for a long time. It was carved by my grand-father, and it shows events in the history of Puerto Rico. See, here are the Indians, Columbus, Ponce de León."[1]

The children surrounded her. "Turn it slowly, and tell more about it, like you tell me, Mamá," said Santiago. So she did, and proudly went on telling the story of her country.

[1] Ponce de León (PON-seh de lay-OHN)

"It is like hearing a book read aloud," said Miss Taylor, when she had finished. She understood now why Santiago lived in two places at once.

"We must go, Señora Román. This has been a day of surprises. I do want to thank you. It was generous of Santiago to invite us here."

"Our house is your house, but it is a fine day for eating lunch by the river. Enjoy it." Santiago's mother opened the door and the children filed out.

"*Gracias*![1] Thank you!" they chorused.

Once outside, they crossed the street and went skipping past the Hispanic Museum. Ahead, lunch bags swinging, feet marching to the beat of a mutual whistling tune, went Santiago and Ernie. On down the long block they marched, on and on towards Riverside Drive and the Hudson River.

Yes, it was a very fine day indeed for eating with one's friends by the river.

[1] *Gracias* (GRAH-see-ahs)

—*Pura Belpré*

What Do You Think?

1. How did Santiago feel about Selina?

2. Why was Santiago eager to have Ernie visit his home?

3. Why did Ernie feel different toward Santiago after seeing Selina?

Taking A Closer Look

1. Where did Santiago and his family come from?

2. Why did Santiago bring a signed permission slip to school?

3. What is a stereoscope? What do you have in school that is like a stereoscope?

4. How did Rosina happen to be in a city parking lot?

5. Why was Santiago so excited when he saw Rosina?

6. What did the gourd in Santiago's home help the children understand?

7. Why did Miss Taylor compare Santiago's mother's story to a book?

Annie has a special reason for not wanting to grow. Her love for the Old One makes her want to keep things exactly the way they are. So she tries to hold back time. What does Annie learn as she tries to make time "stand still"?

Annie and the Old One

Annie's Navajo world was good—a world of rippling sand, of high copper-red bluffs in the distance, of the low mesa near her own snug hogan. The pumpkins were yellow in the cornfield, and the tassels on the corn were turning brown.

Each morning, the gate to the night pen near the hogan was opened wide and the sheep were herded to pasture on the desert.

Annie helped watch the sheep. She carried pails of water to the cornfield. And every weekday, she walked to the bus stop and waited for the yellow bus that took her to school and brought her home again.

Best of all were the evenings when she sat at her grandmother's feet and listened to stories of times long gone.

Sometimes it seemed to Annie that her grandmother was her age—a girl who had seen no more than nine or ten harvestings.

If a mouse scampered across the hard dirt floor of their hogan, Annie and her grandmother laughed together.

And when they prepared the fried bread for the evening meal, if it burned a bit black at the edges, they laughed and said it was good.

There were other times when her grandmother sat small and still, and Annie knew that she was very old. Then Annie would cover the thin knees of the Old One with a warm blanket. It was at such a time that her grandmother said, "It is time you learn to weave, my granddaughter."

Annie touched the web of wrinkles that crisscrossed her grandmother's face and slowly went outside the hogan. Beside the door, her father sat cross-legged, working with silver and fire, making a handsome, heavy necklace. Annie passed him and went to the big loom where her mother sat weaving.

Annie sat beside the loom, watching, while her mother slid the weaving stick in place among the strings of the warp. With red wool, her mother added a row to a slanting arrow of red, bright against the dull background.

Annie's thoughts wandered. She thought about the stories her grandmother had told—stories of hardship when rains flooded the desert—of dry weather when rains did not fall and the pumpkins and corn were dry in the field. Annie looked out across the sand where the cactus bore its red fruit, and thought about the coyote—God's Dog—guarding the scattered hogans of the Navajos.

Annie watched while her mother worked. She made herself sit very still. After a time, her mother looked at her and smiled. "Are you ready to weave, my daughter?"

Annie shook her head. She continued to watch while her mother twisted the weaving stick in the warp, making a shed for the strands of gray and red wool.

At last her mother said softly, "You may go," almost as though she knew what Annie wanted.

Annie ran off to find her grandmother, and together they gathered twigs and brush to feed the small fire in the middle of the hogan. When the evening meal was done, the old grandmother called her family together.

Annie and her mother and father stood quietly, respectfully, waiting for the grandmother to speak. A coyote called shrilly from the mesa. There was no sound in the hogan. There was no sound at all, except a small snap of the dying fire. Then the grandmother spoke softly.

"My children, when the new rug is taken from the loom, I will go to Mother Earth."

Annie shivered and looked at her mother. Her mother's eyes were shining bright with tears that did not fall, and Annie knew what her grandmother meant. Her heart stood still and she made no sound. The Old One spoke again.

"You will each choose the gift you wish to have."

Annie looked at the hard earth, swept smooth and clean.

"What will you have, my granddaughter?" the grandmother asked.

Annie looked at a weaving stick propped against the wall of the hogan. This was the grandmother's own weaving stick, polished and beautiful with age. Annie looked directly at the stick. As though Annie had spoken, her grandmother nodded.

"My granddaughter shall have my weaving stick."

On the floor of the hogan lay a rug that the Old One had woven long, long ago. Its colors were soft and beautiful. Annie's mother chose the rug. Annie's father chose the silver belt studded with turquoise that was now loose around the small waist of the Old One.

Annie folded her arms tightly across her stomach and went outside, and her mother followed.

"How can my grandmother know she will go to Mother Earth when the rug is taken from the loom?" Annie asked.

"Many of the Old Ones know," her mother said.

"How do they know?"

"Your grandmother is one of those who live in harmony with all nature—with earth, coyote, birds in the sky. They know more than many will ever learn. Those Old Ones know." Her mother sighed deeply. "We will speak of other things."

In the days that followed, the grandmother went about her work much as she had always done. She ground corn to make meal for bread. She gathered dry twigs and brush to make fire. And when there was no school, she and Annie watched the sheep and listened to the sweet, clear music of the bell on the collar of the lead goat.

The weaving of the rug was high on the loom. It was almost as high as Annie's waist.

"My mother," Annie said, "why do you weave?"

"I weave so we may sell the rug and buy the things we must have from the trading post. Silver for silver-making. Deer hide for boots—"

"But you know what my grandmother said—"

Annie's mother did not speak. She slid her weaving stick through the warp and picked up a strand of rose-red wool. Annie turned and ran. She ran across the sand and huddled in the shallow shade of the small mesa. Her grandmother would go back to the earth when the rug was taken from the loom. The rug must not be finished. Her mother must not weave.

The next morning, where her grandmother went, Annie followed. When it was time to go to the bus stop to meet the school bus, she walked very slowly, watching her feet. Perhaps she would miss the bus.

And then quite suddenly she did not want to miss it. She knew what she must do. She ran hard, as fast as she could — breathing deeply — and the yellow bus was waiting for her at the stop. She climbed aboard. The bus moved on, stopping now and then at hogans along the way. Annie sat there alone and made her plan.

In school, she would be bad, so bad that the teacher would send for her mother and father. And if her mother and father came to school to talk to the teacher, that would be one day when her mother could not weave. One day.

On the playground, Annie's teacher was in charge of the girls' gymnasium class.

"Who will lead the exercises today?" the teacher asked.

No one answered.

The teacher laughed. "Very well. Then I shall be leader." The teacher was young. Her blue skirt was wide and the heels on her brown shoes were high. The teacher kicked off her shoes and the girls laughed.

Annie followed the teacher's lead — bending, jumping, and she waited for the time when the teacher would lead them in jogging around the playground. As Annie jogged past the spot where the teacher's shoes lay on the ground, she picked up a shoe and hid it in the folds of her dress. And when Annie jogged past a trash can, she dropped the shoe inside.

Some of the girls saw her and laughed, but some frowned and were serious. When the line jogged near the schoolhouse door, Annie slipped from the line and went inside to her room and her own desk. Clearly she heard the teacher as she spoke to the girls outside.

"The other shoe, please." Her voice was pleasant. There was silence.

Limping, one shoe on and one shoe gone, the teacher came into the room. The girls followed, giggling and holding their hands across their mouths.

"I know it's funny," the teacher said, "but now I need the shoe."

Annie looked at the boards of the floor. A shiny black beetle crawled between the cracks.

The door opened and a man teacher came inside with a shoe in his hand. As he passed Annie's desk, he touched her shoulder and smiled down at her.

"I saw someone playing tricks," he said.

The teacher looked at Annie and the room was very still. When school was over for the day, Annie waited. Timidly, with hammering heart, she went to the teacher's desk.

"Do you want my mother and father to come to the school tomorrow?" she asked.

"No, Annie," the teacher said. "I have the shoe. Everything is all right."

Annie's face was hot and her hands were cold. She turned and ran. She was the last to climb on the bus. Finally, there was her own bus stop. She hopped down and slowly trudged the long way home. She stopped beside the loom. The rug was now much higher than her waist.

That night she curled up in her blanket. She slept lightly, and awakened before dawn. There was no sound from her mother's sheepskin. Her grandmother was a quiet hump in her blanket. Annie heard only her father's loud, sleeping breathing. There was no other sound on the whole earth, except the howling of a coyote from far across the desert.

In the dim light of early morning, Annie crept outside to the night pen where the sheep were sleeping. The dry wood creaked when she opened the gate and pushed it wide open against the fence.

She tugged at the sleeping sheep until one stood quietly. Then the others stood also, uncertain — shoving together. The lead goat turned toward the open gate and Annie slipped her fingers through his belled collar. She curled her fingertips across the bell, muffling its sound, and led the goat through the gate. The sheep followed.

She led them across the sand and around the small mesa where she let go of the goat.

"Go," she said.

She ran back to the hogan, and crept under her blanket and lay shivering. Now her family would hunt the sheep all day. This would be a day when her mother would not weave.

When the fullness of morning came and it was light, Annie watched her grandmother rise and go outside. Annie heard her call.

"The sheep are gone."

Annie's mother and father hurried outside and Annie followed.

Her mother moaned very softly, "The sheep—the sheep—"

"I see them," the grandmother said. "They graze near the mesa."

Annie went with her grandmother and when they reached the sheep, Annie's fingers slipped under the goat's collar and the bell tingled sharply as the sheep followed back to the pen.

In school that day, Annie sat quietly and wondered what more she could do. When the teacher asked questions, Annie looked at the floor. She did not even hear.

When night came, she curled up in her blanket, but not to sleep. When everything was still, she slipped from her blanket and crept outside. The sky was dark and secret. The wind was soft against her face. For a moment she stood waiting until she could see in the night. She went to the loom.

She felt for the weaving stick there in its place among the warp strings. She separated the warp and felt for the wool. Slowly she pulled out the strands of yarn, one by one.

One by one, she laid them across her knees. And when the row was removed, she separated the strings of the warp again, and reached for the second row.

When the woven rug was only as high as her waist, she crept back to her blanket, taking the strands of wool with her. Under her blanket, she smoothed the strands and made them into a ball. And then she slept.

The next night, Annie removed another day's weaving.

In the morning when her mother went to the loom, she looked at the weaving—puzzled. For a moment, she pressed her fingers against her eyes. The Old One looked at Annie curiously. Annie held her breath.

The third night, Annie crept to the loom. A gentle hand touched her shoulder.

"Go to sleep, my granddaughter," the Old One said.

Annie wanted to throw her arms around her grandmother's waist and tell her why she had been bad, but she could only stumble to her blanket and huddle under it and let the tears roll into the edge of her hair.

When morning came, Annie unrolled herself from the blanket and helped prepare the morning meal. Afterward, she followed her grandmother through the cornfield. Her grandmother walked slowly, and Annie fitted her steps to the slow steps of the Old One.

When they reached the small mesa, the Old One sat crossing her knees. She folded her wrinkled fingers into her lap. Annie knelt beside her. The Old One looked far off toward the edge of the desert where sky met sand.

"My granddaughter," she said, "you have tried to hold back time. This cannot be done." The desert stretched yellow and brown away to the edge of the morning sky. "The sun comes up from the edge of earth in the morning. It returns to the edge of earth in the evening. Earth, from which good things come for the living creatures on it. Earth, to which all creatures finally go."

Annie picked up a handful of brown sand and pressed it against the palm of her hand. Slowly, she let it fall to earth. She understood many things.

The sun rose but it also set. The cactus did not bloom forever. Petals dried and fell to earth.

She knew that she was a part of the earth and the things on it. She would always be a part of the earth, just as her grandmother had always been, just as her grandmother would always be, always and forever.

And Annie was breathless with the wonder of it.

They walked back to the hogan together, Annie and the Old One. Annie picked up the old weaving stick.

"I am ready to weave," she said to her mother. "I will use the stick that my grandmother has given me." She knelt at the loom.

She separated the warp strings and slipped the weaving stick in place, as her mother had done, as her grandmother had done. She picked up a strand of gray wool and started to weave.

—*Miska Miles*

What Do You Think?

1. Why did Annie feel a special love for her grandmother?

2. Do you think her grandmother did the best thing when she gathered the family together after supper? Explain.

3. After that, why didn't Annie's grandmother scold Annie when she misbehaved?

4. How did her grandmother finally help Annie understand about "going to Mother Earth"?

Taking A Closer Look

1. Tell some of the reasons Annie enjoyed being with her grandmother.

2. Why did Annie try at first to miss the school bus?

3. How do you think the teacher should have treated Annie when she hid the shoe?

4. How did Annie try to "hold back time"?

5. How did Annie show she finally understood what her grandmother had been telling her?

My People

I am a Navajo, the Navajos are my people.
They live in the hogans upon the dry desert,
With a little shade house and a sheep corral.
It is nice and peaceful there away
From the city street.
There were the sad, dark years for my people,
But my people didn't disappear.
They started rebuilding, increasing
In population.
I am proud that the desert floor,
The lonely hogans,
Have made me thoughtful and
Respectful of my people.
I am proud to be born in my people's land.
I shall never forget my home and people.

—Bernice George

Aha!
A Sleuth!

Sleuth is another name for a detective. Sleuths wake up every morning with one thought in mind—solve the case! They think of nothing else. A good sleuth asks questions, finds clues, and puts them all together to find the answer. Sleuths are all eye and brain— curious and determined.

As you read the stories in this unit, watch for clues. Put on your sleuth cap and try to be the first one to find the answers.

Sometimes four eyes work much better than just two, especially if one pair of them is cat-eyes. Meet Hash San,[1] the sleuth-cat who helps Kathi. Together they discover that having all the clues in the bag doesn't solve the case. What does?

[1] Hash San (HAHSH san)

Kathi and Hash San

The Case of Measles

More than anything Kathi wanted to be a detective. She had a notebook and pencil. She had a clue bag to keep important clues in. But she didn't have a case.

The Deadeye Detective Club had lots of cases. But—

"Don't bother us," said Ben.

"Theodore's lost," said Len.

"Theodore who?" asked Kathi.

"We're looking for clues," said Henry.

"I'll help you look," said Kathi.

"A girl detective?" said Ben.

"Get lost," said Henry.

And Ben, Len, and Henry slammed the clubhouse door. BANG!

Kathi still wanted to be a detective. She still had her notebook and pencil. But she didn't have any notes.

She still had her clue bag. But she didn't have any clues. She still needed a case. She sat on her front steps. She sighed. Where was she going to find a case to solve?

Measles came and sat beside her. Measles looked sad.

"Trouble," he said. "Big bad trouble!"

Now Kathi could do one thing nobody in the Deadeye Detective Club could do. She could talk to cats. Wise old Hash San had taught her. And so she said,

"What kind of trouble, Measles?"

"The Browns are going to give me away," he wailed. "All because of that dumb bird."

"But I thought you *liked* him," said Kathi. "I thought you and Max were pals."

"Not Max," said Measles. "Tiny. He flew in the window last Tuesday. And he brought big bad trouble with him."

"How big?" asked Kathi. "How bad?"

"The Browns think I knock over his cage," said Measles. "And open his door. And scare him."

"Why do the Browns think you do all that?" asked Kathi.

"Because I'm there every time it happens," said Measles.

"Well," said Kathi, "if you're there, can't you see who's doing it?"

"But I'm asleep every time!" wailed Measles.

"Hey!" said Kathi. "That's a mystery!"

She wrote in her notebook. Like this:

The Measles Mystery.
Somebody knocks over Tiny's cage.
Somebody scares him. Measles
is asleep. Who does it?
a crook?
a birdnapper?
a bird hater?

Kathi closed her notebook. "I'll take your case," she said. "I'll get to work on it right away."

"Thanks," said Measles. "I hope you solve it before the Browns give me away."

Kathi wanted to be a detective more than anything. And now she had a case to solve. So she went to see her friend Hash San.

Hash was short for Hashimoto.[1] *San* means "Mister" in Japanese. Mister Hashimoto was a long, hard name to say. But Hash San was just right for a wise old Japanese cat.

Hash San was sitting on the bridge over the goldfish pond behind the Fuji[2] Tea House.

"Oh," he said, "a young friend comes to visit an old friend."

Kathi told him about Measles and Tiny.

"Birds of a feather are not always happy together," said Hash San.

"You mean Max and Tiny?" asked Kathi.

"Sharp eyes will find many clues at the scene of the crime," said Hash San.

"But how can we get to the scene of the crime—I mean, into the Browns' house?" asked Kathi.

"A good detective finds a way," said Hash San.

Kathi was a good detective. She tried to find a way. She tried . . . and she tried . . . and she tried. . . . But she couldn't find a way to get into the Browns' house.

[1] Hashimoto (HAH-shee-moh-toh) [2] Fuji (FOO-jee)

But—Kathi was a good detective. She thought and she thought till she thought of a good idea. She made a sign. It said:

Odd jobs. Anywhere. Anytime. 25¢

She put the sign on Mrs. Brown's door.

When Mrs. Brown saw the sign she called, "Oh, Kathi, will you feed Measles and Max and Tiny tomorrow? We're going away overnight."

"Yes, ma'am," said Kathi.

"But don't let Measles inside unless you're with him," said Mrs. Brown. "He's been very mean to Tiny."

Poor Measles! Kathi was glad he didn't hear that!

In the morning Kathi and Hash San went to the Browns'. Measles was sitting on the back steps. He was very wet.

"It's been raining dogs and pups," he said. "And I was left out all night. All because of that dumb bird."

Poor, poor Measles! Measles followed Kathi and Hash San into the house. He jumped up on the kitchen

table. He sat among the cans of cat food and the boxes of birdseed and the paper for Tiny's cage. He began to lick himself dry.

"I'd better feed Measles first," Kathi whispered to Hash San.

"That's very wise," Hash San whispered back. "A full stomach makes a heavy heart light."

Kathi set out liver and sardines and shrimp. Then she and Hash San went into the living room.

Tiny was hopping around in his cage. "Cheep," he cheeped.

Max was hanging upside down on the lamp.

"Pretty Max," he squawked.

Kathi changed the paper in Tiny's cage. She set out birdseed for Tiny and sunflower seed for Max.

"Too bad you birds can't really talk," she said.

"If birds give us a bird's-eye view," said Hash San, "then there is no need for private eyes."

"And I wouldn't have a case to solve," said Kathi.

Kathi and Hash San went back to the kitchen to get water for Tiny and Max. Hash San looked around.

"The dish is empty," he said. "Also the kitchen."

"But Measles was here a few minutes ago," said Kathi.

CRASH!

"Wherever the crash is," said Hash San, "that's where Measles is! Come!"

90

They ran to the living room. There he was all right. And—Tiny's cage was empty! It rolled on the floor.

"Cheep!" cheeped Tiny from the curtain rod.

"Squawk!" squawked Max from the lamp.

"I didn't do it!" yelled Measles from the armchair. "I was sound asleep."

Kathi picked up the cage.

"Wait," said Hash San.

"A good detective may now find good clues at the scene of the crime."

Kathi was a good detective. She set down the cage and looked for clues.

Clue Number 1 was on the armchair. Hash San found two cat hairs there.

"See?" said Measles. "That proves I was in this chair."

Kathi dropped the cat hairs into her clue bag.

Clue Number 2 was in Tiny's cage. Hash San found that one, too. "The paper tells the news," he said.

Kathi looked. There on the clean white paper was a cat's paw print!

Measles looked, too.

"It doesn't prove a thing," he said. "I didn't go near that cage."

Carefully Kathi tore off the paw print and dropped it into her clue bag.

Kathi was a good detective. And Kathi found Clue Number 3. She found it when she put Tiny back into his cage.

"Look!" she said. "Tiny must have caught his tail in the cage door."

Hash San looked.

"You have seen what I did not see," he said.

Kathi felt proud.

"The feather in the cage door can unlock the mystery," said Hash San.

Kathi put the feather into her clue bag.

"What about the paw print?" she asked.

"Don't forget the cat hairs," said Measles.

"All the clues are in the bag," said Hash San. "But the case is not in the bag—yet."

The rain had stopped. Kathi let Measles out.

"It's wet, wet, wet," he grumbled.

Kathi and Hash San sat in the sun on the back steps. Hash San closed his eyes. Was he asleep? Kathi knew better. He was thinking.

The tip of Measles' tail went tap-tap-tap on the step.

Suddenly Hash San's eyes opened wide.

"That feather means trouble for Tiny!" he said. "Back to the living room. Rush!"

But Tiny was still safe in his cage. Max was asleep on the lamp.

"So," said Hash San, "trouble for Tiny comes only when Measles comes."

"I guess Tiny's trouble *is* Measles," said Kathi.

"Detectives do not guess," said Hash San. "Detectives must be sure. Tonight we will find out, for sure."

Hash San had a plan. He told Kathi his plan.

Then he went back to the Fuji Tea House to watch the goldfish. And Kathi went home to watch TV.

After supper that night, Kathi went to the Browns'. Hash San met her there. She opened three kinds of cat food—liver, sardines, and shrimp.

But Measles wouldn't eat. He pointed to Hash San.

"He thinks I did it," he said.

Hash San looked away.

Measles pointed to Kathi.

"You think I did it," he said.

Kathi looked away.

"It isn't fair," sighed Measles. "I'm losing my happy home because of something I didn't do!"

And he didn't touch his food. Not the liver, nor the sardines, nor the shrimp.

Kathi and Hash San went into the living room to feed Max and Tiny. Measles followed them.

"Can I rest here in my armchair before you throw me out?" he asked.

"You can rest there all night," said Kathi.

"That's kind of you," said Measles. "But I couldn't sleep a wink."

Two minutes later he was snoring. And two minutes after that Max and Tiny tucked their heads under their wings and went to sleep, too.

"Good," said Hash San. "Our plan is working. Now to make noisy noise on our way out."

Hash San dropped a cookie pan. Clang! Kathi slammed the back door. Bang!

Then they tiptoed around to the front porch and looked in the picture window. They watched Measles sleeping in the armchair. They watched Tiny sleeping in his cage. They watched Max sleeping on the lamp.

"It's like watching TV," said Kathi.

"Only it's real," said Hash San.

Kathi yawned.

"I'm getting sleepy," she said.

Suddenly the sleepy picture in the picture window changed. Max woke up and flew to Tiny's cage. He opened the door with his beak! Tiny flew out. Then Max knocked over the cage!

"It was Max all the time!" said Kathi. "Not Measles! Quick! Stop him."

"Wait," said Hash San. "And watch. Max will not hurt Tiny."

Max flew to an open window. He stuck his head out and yowled and howled.

"Why," said Kathi, "he sounds just like Measles!"

But they could see Measles. He was sound asleep in the armchair. Then Tiny started to fly toward the open window.

"He'll fly out!" said Kathi.

"Now! We must stop the trouble," said Hash San.

Kathi and Hash San ran into the living room. Kathi shut the window just in time. Measles was awake at last.

"I didn't do it!" he yelled.

"We know you didn't," said Kathi.

"We watched Max do it," said Hash San.

Measles fell out of the armchair.

"My old pal Max," he said.

"Pal Max must be Number One Bird," said Hash San. "To stay Number One, he must get rid of Tiny."

"But he made the Browns think you did all those things, Measles," said Kathi.

"So!" said Hash San. "Tiny goes . . . The Browns blame Measles. Measles must go, and Max stays— Number One Bird *and* Number One Pet."

Measles climbed back into the armchair to think. His tail went thump-thump-thump.

"Big bad trouble," he muttered.

"Hash San," said Kathi, "what about Clue Number Two? Didn't Measles leave that paw print?"

"Please follow me," said Hash San.

They went to the kitchen.

"Make believe it is this morning," said Hash San.

"Measles followed us inside," said Kathi.

"Wet from the rain," grumbled Measles.

Hash San pointed to the table.

"Food and cage paper were there," he said.

"And so was Measles!" said Kathi.

"Lying on the table," said Hash San, "washing his muddy paws."

"That's when he left his paw print on the paper," said Kathi. "*Before* we put it in the cage!"

"That is right!" said Hash San. "But Clue Number Three unlocks the mystery. The parakeet feather in the parakeet cage—good. But the *parrot* feather in the parakeet cage—not good. Clue Number Three makes Max Suspect Number One."

"And I thought it was Tiny's feather!" said Kathi.

"Pretty Max," squawked Max.

"Poor old Max," said Measles. "I feel kind of sorry for him."

"But he almost got you thrown out of your happy home," said Kathi.

"We were pals," said Measles, "until that dumb bird flew in the window."

"Measles and Max could be pals again," said Hash San.

The mystery was solved. Kathi and Hash San went home. They left Measles asleep in his armchair and Max asleep on the lamp.

Kathi took Tiny with her.

Mrs. Brown came home the next day. Kathi told her about Max.

"Oh, dear," said Mrs. Brown. "Well, if Measles can forgive Max—and us—we'll keep them both. But what shall I do with Tiny?"

"There's a lady down the street," said Kathi. "She has ten parakeets."

"Maybe she wouldn't mind one more," said Mrs. Brown.

Down the street on the parakeet lady's porch Kathi counted the whole Deadeye Detective Club—Ben, Len, and Henry. And in a big green cage on the porch Kathi counted ten—no, only *nine* parakeets!

"Theodore!" cried the lady, running down the porch steps. "You found Theodore!"

"She found Theodore!" yelled Ben.

The lady took Tiny.

"Where have you been, Theodore?" she cried.

"Cheep," cheeped Tiny-Theodore.

The lady hugged Kathi. Kathi tried to tell her she hadn't really found Theodore. But the lady didn't listen. She was busy putting Theodore back in the big green cage with her nine other parakeets.

Kathi tried to tell Ben, Len, and Henry. But they didn't listen either. They just kept on asking questions about how she had found Theodore.

Kathi gave up.

She went down to the Fuji Tea House and sat on the bridge with wise old Hash San.

More than anything Kathi had wanted to be a detective. She had needed a case. She had found one— and solved it — The Case of Measles.

—*Jean Lewis*

What Do You Think?

1. Why did Kathi think Hash San was a very special friend?
2. What reason did Max have for committing the crime?
3. What do you think of Kathi as a detective?

Taking A Closer Look

1. Why didn't the Deadeye Detective Club want Kathi's help with their case?
2. What problem did Measles bring to Kathi?
3. What facts did Kathi have at the beginning of the case?
4. What was Kathi's plan for getting into the Brown's house?
5. What clues did Kathi and Hash San find?
6. Which of the clues proved to be the most important? Why?
7. When did the author first let you know Max was a parrot?
8. What was the second mystery Kathi and Hash San solved?
9. How did Kathi discover who Theodore was?

CAT

My cat
Is quiet.
She moves without a sound.
Sometimes she stretches herself high and curving
On tiptoe.
Sometimes she crouches low
And creeping.

Sometimes she rubs herself against a chair,
And there
    With a *miew* and a *miew*
    And a purrrr   purrrr   purrrr
    She curls up
    And goes to sleep.

My cat
Lives through a black hole
Under the house.
So one day I
Crawled in after her.

And it was dark
And I sat
And didn't know
Where to go.
And then—

Two yellow-white
Round little lights
Came moving . . . moving . . . toward
  me.
And there
With a *miew* and a *miew*
And a purrrr   purrrr   purrrr
My cat
Rubbed, soft, against me.

And I knew
The lights
Were MY CAT'S EYES
In the dark.

—*Dorothy Baruch*

103

Is a brain full of facts from A to Z enough to solve the case? Eyes, ears, and a sniffing nose may help too. Watch for hints. See if you can solve the case before you read the answer. Try sniffing out the clue.

The Case of
Nellie and the Ambergris

Dinner at the Browns' red brick house in Idaville was not like dinner in other homes.

The Browns not only broke bread together. They broke crimes together.

Mr. Brown was chief of police. People everywhere thought that he was the brains behind Idaville's wonderful record of law and order.

Nobody could have guessed the truth. Behind Chief Brown's success was his only child—ten-year-old Encyclopedia.

Chief Brown brought home his hardest cases. Encyclopedia solved them while eating dinner. Since he had begun secretly helping his father, no crook had escaped arrest, and no child had got away with ducking the law.

Chief Brown would have liked to pin a medal on Encyclopedia every time his son solved a case. But what good would it do?

Who would believe that the real mastermind behind Idaville's crime cleanup was a fifth grader?

Besides, Encyclopedia couldn't have stood up under all the medals without getting flat feet.

So Chief Brown said nothing.

Encyclopedia never let slip a word about the help he gave his father. He did not want to seem different from other boys.

However, there was nothing he could do about his nickname.

Only his parents and teachers called him by his right name, Leroy. Everyone else called him Encyclopedia.

An encyclopedia is a book or set of books full of facts from A to Z—like Encyclopedia's brain. He had done more reading than just about anybody in town. His pals said that when he turned a cartwheel, his head sounded like a bookcase falling over.

Encyclopedia helped his father solve mysteries at the dinner table all year around. In the summer, he helped the children of the neighborhood as well.

When school let out, he opened his own detective agency in the garage. Every morning he hung out his sign:

BROWN DETECTIVE AGENCY
13 ROVER AVENUE
LEROY BROWN, PRESIDENT
NO CASE TOO SMALL
25¢ PER DAY
PLUS EXPENSES

One day Smelly Nellie came into the garage. She was only nine years old. Yet she already had earned the money for her college education.

She had done it with her nose alone.

When she was eight, she had saved the city hall from being blown to kingdom come. She had sniffed out a leak in the gas line running into the building just as Mr. Barnes, the mayor, was about to light a cigar nearby.

As a reward, the city council had set aside money to pay her way through the college of her choice.

After that, no one called her by her real name, Nelita Theodora Shortridge. Everyone called her Smelly Nellie for short.

Her nose didn't stop at sniffing gas leaks. It could smell a marshmallow roast—or anything else—three blocks away, rain or shine.

When she came into the Brown Detective Agency, however, she wasn't using her nose. She was holding it.

"Ambergris," she gagged.

Encyclopedia had read about ambergris. It is thrown up by sick whales. It is found floating in southern waters and is used in making perfume.

"Don't just sit there," piped Smelly Nellie. "Bring a bottle of oil of peppermint!"

Encyclopedia jumped to it. Within twenty seconds he was shoving an open bottle under Smelly Nellie's wonderful nose. She breathed deeply.

"Thanks," she sighed. "It's the only thing to clear the passages."

"What snarled the sneezer?" asked Encyclopedia.

"Did you ever stand close to ambergris?" asked Smelly Nellie. "It's worse than being scorekeeper at a skunk fight."

She laid twenty-five cents on the gas can beside Encyclopedia.

"I want you to get back my ambergris," she said. "Bugs Meany stole it!"

"Give Bugs a free hand, and he'll stick it right into your pocket," said Encyclopedia.

Bugs Meany was the leader of a gang of tough older boys. Encyclopedia had often been hired to stop their stealing and cheating.

"Let's go speak with Bugs," said Encyclopedia.

The two children took the Number 7 bus. During the ride, Smelly Nellie told her story.

She had found the ambergris washed up on the beach at Lighthouse Point that morning while she was smelling for clams.

"Bugs Meany and his Tigers were skin diving offshore," she said. "I asked them to help me get the stuff home."

The Tigers had laughed and told her to go chase herself. So Smelly Nellie had to tell them the truth. A company in New York City was paying five dollars an ounce for ambergris.

"I found a lump that must weigh fifty pounds," she said.

Encyclopedia whistled and did some figuring: sixteen times fifty times five—four thousand dollars!

"That's enough money to buy a car," he said.

"Bugs Meany thought the same," said Smelly Nellie. "When he heard what ambergris is worth, he asked me if I thought he'd look good in a sports car. Then he told me to scram."

The bus halted at the last stop, and the children got off. They walked along the beach toward Lighthouse Point.

After about a mile, Smelly Nellie gave a cry and pinched her nose. Encyclopedia took the warning and did likewise.

Another few steps brought them around a bend. They saw the lighthouse and the Tigers.

The Tigers had done no more than beach their boat. They were lying on their backs, holding their noses and groaning.

The lump of ambergris was still on the wet sand at the high-tide line. It looked like a ball of dark-gray wax.

"The Tigers haven't got away with the stuff yet," said Smelly Nellie gleefully. "The smell flattened 'em!"

Bugs Meany was the first to see Smelly Nellie and the boy detective. He shouted the alarm and sat up weakly.

"Beat it," he growled at Encyclopedia. "Or I'll yank your tongue so hard your ears will roll up like window shades."

Encyclopedia was used to Bug's greeting. "The ambergris belongs to Smelly Nellie," he said. "She found the lump this morning."

"Me and my Tigers found the lump on the bottom of the ocean while we were skin diving," retorted Bugs.

"Then how did it get on the beach?" demanded Encyclopedia.

"We rolled it under the water," replied Bugs Meany. "Then we waited for the tide to go out so we could lift it into the boat."

"You're lying!" said Smelly Nellie.

"And I can prove it," added Encyclopedia.

HOW?

(For the solution, turn to the next page.)

111

Solution to the Case of
Nellie and the Ambergris

Bugs Meany was weak from the smell of ambergris. So he wasn't thinking too clearly when Encyclopedia questioned him.

And he knew nothing about ambergris except what Smelly Nellie had told him—that it was worth five dollars an ounce.

Bugs said his Tigers had found the ambergris on the ocean bottom while skin diving. Then they had rolled the lump near the shore and waited for the tide to go out.

That was the lie that gave him away!

Ambergris doesn't sink to the bottom of the ocean.

As Encyclopedia knew, it is found *floating* on the water.

Bugs returned the ambergris to the rightful owner, Smelly Nellie.

—*Donald J. Sobol*

What Do You Think?

1. What do you think it was like to be a member of the Brown Family?

2. How would you describe Leroy Brown to a friend who had never met him?

3. All the children in the story had nick-names. The author tells you why Nelita Theodora Shortridge was called Smelly Nellie and why Leroy Brown was called Encyclopedia. But why was the leader of the Tigers called Bugs Meany?

Taking A Closer Look

1. Why did Encyclopedia want to keep his talents a secret?

2. How did Leroy Brown spend his summers?

3. How was Nellie rewarded for saving the mayor?

4. Why did Nellie want to get the ambergris back?

5. Where did Nellie get so much ambergris?

6. How did Bugs Meany and his gang discover the value of the ambergris?

7. What was the first clue Encyclopedia and Nellie discovered at the lighthouse?

8. What clue helped Encyclopedia solve the case?

Clues are everywhere—and so is
trickery! But good sleuths keep
their eyes open and their brains
working. They learn to remember
everything and to sort out
clues. Who's doing what?
How many people are involved?
Join Encyclopedia Brown and
his friend Sally, but keep your
eye on the twins. Watch the
race. Maybe *you'll* come out a
winning sleuth!

The Case of the Blueberry Pies

Encyclopedia was shocked. He had just seen Chester Jenkins *running* past the detective agency.

Chester never ran—except to the school cafeteria at lunch hour. He was the biggest eater in the fifth grade.

He was also the roundest. In fact, Chester was nearly as high lying down as standing up.

Encyclopedia hurried out to the sidewalk. He looked up and down the block. There wasn't an ice cream truck in sight.

"What's wrong, Chester?" he called.

Chester stopped. He turned around and wobbled back. He was puffing like a marching band.

"I'm in training," he gasped. "I have to be in shape for the Idaville Youth Fair tomorrow."

"Charlie Stewart entered his tooth collection in the hobby contest," said Encyclopedia. "Are you in a running race?"

"Not exactly," replied Chester. "I'm getting in trim for the pie-eating contest."

Encyclopedia was puzzled. Why roadwork? Chester was a cinch to win. Only Belly Slave, the hippopotamus at the zoo, could eat more.

"Do you remember how sick the Thompson twins, Jimmy and Johnny, became last year?" asked Chester. "Their mother said the pie-eating contest was disgusting. She said there ought to be a physical fitness contest instead."

Encyclopedia remembered last year. Chester had left the other boys lying on their backs covered with pie crumbs. The Thompson twins had to be carried home.

"The rules have been changed," said Chester. "This year each boy has only two pies to eat. But he must run half a mile to the finish line."

"Hopping hamburgers!" exclaimed Encyclopedia. "That's a tough break, Chester."

"Those Thompson twins are fast runners," said Chester. "But if apple pie is used, I'll have a good chance. Apple pie is my favorite."

"Here's to apple pie!" said Encyclopedia.

"Thanks," said Chester, and grimly resumed his running.

The next morning Encyclopedia and Sally biked to the Idaville Youth Fair. It was a city of tents and fun rides crowded into one corner of the old airstrip.

The two detectives watched the kite-flying contest and the pet show. At ten o'clock a whistle blew for the pie-eating contest.

Fifteen boys lined up to hear Mrs. Thompson, the mother of the twins. She explained the new rules.

Each boy was to race to the table opposite him. On each table were two pies. The boys were to eat the pies, using the knives and forks provided, and then run a half-mile course among the tents.

"Most of the running will be out of view of the judges," said Mrs. Thompson. "But a father will be stationed every two hundred yards to make sure no boy takes a short cut."

The knives and forks troubled Encyclopedia. "Last year Chester won bare-handed," he said to Sally. "Table manners will slow him down."

"The silverware is Mrs. Thompson's idea," said Sally. "She said eating with the hands is a disgrace."

"Chester still has a chance if the pies are made with apples," said Encyclopedia. "Apple pie is his favorite."

"They're blueberry pies," said Sally. "Mrs. Thompson baked them herself. She said she didn't want anyone getting sick."

Encyclopedia saw Chester's chances fading as the boys crouched at the starting line.

"On your marks," said Mrs. Thompson. "Get set . . . go!"

Fifteen boys dashed for the tables.

Chester got off to a bad start. He was the last to reach the pies, and he fumbled his knife and fork.

After the first mouthful, however, he settled down. He began to eat smoothly, showing the form which had won him last year's contest. Knife and fork flashed like lightning. He overtook the other boys rapidly.

"He's ahead!" screamed Sally. "Go, Chester!"

"Say," said Encyclopedia, frowning. "I see only one of the Thompson twins."

Sally looked at the pie eaters carefully. "You're right," she said. "Which twin is missing, Jimmy or Johnny?"

"Don't ask me," said Encyclopedia. "I can't tell them apart. Come on, Chester!"

Chester was eating like a true champion. He was the first to finish both pies. He wiped his face and started on the half-mile course. In a moment he was lost behind the rows of tents.

The second boy to finish eating was the Thompson twin. He wiped his face, jumped from the table, and sprinted after Chester.

Three other boys finished their pies. But they could not run more than ten feet. The rest gave up at the table.

The race was between Chester and the twin!

"Chester has a minute headstart," whooped Sally. "There's nobody who can hold his pies like Chester!"

So it seemed as Chester eventually staggered into view again, still leading. Ahead of him stretched one hundred yards of open ground to the finish line.

He was halfway there when the onlookers roared. The twin had burst into view, running like the wind.

Chester was wobbling gamely, but slowing down with every step. The twin sped past him and won by fifteen yards. Encyclopedia and Sally were stunned.

121

When the twin had caught his breath, he walked back and forth, shaking hands. His lips were parted in a wide smile of victory.

"He sure has beautiful teeth," said Sally grudgingly. "Look at him strut. You'd think he was on television doing a toothpaste commercial."

Encyclopedia stared bitterly at the twin's white-toothed smile.

"He'll be smiling on the other side of his face soon," said the boy detective. "Chester is the rightful winner."

"Did the twin cheat?" said Sally.

"The *twins* cheated," said Encyclopedia.

WHAT MADE ENCYCLOPEDIA
SO SURE?

—*Donald J. Sobol*

What Do You Think?

1. What made this contest different from most pie-eating contests?

2. How do you feel about entering contests?

3. How do you think Chester felt when the twin won the contest?

Taking A Closer Look

1. With an appetite like Chester's, why did he need to train for a pie-eating contest?

2. Why were the rules for the contest changed?

3. Why were the fathers stationed along the path of the race?

4. What made Encyclopedia suspicious of the twins at the beginning of the contest?

5. Who were the two finalists in the contest?

6. What surprising thing happened when the race was nearly over?

7. What was the clue that helped Encyclopedia solve the mystery?

Who would *want* to kidnap an old, fat, lazy dog? But Fletcher *is* missing! To solve this mystery, you will need to watch for false clues, and to "detect" the real ones. Does Fletcher's personality give you a clue? Are you getting better at sleuthing? See for yourself!

Something Strange Is Going On

One day Jill came home and Fletcher wasn't there.

Jill asked Linda, the woman who took care of her during the day, "Have you seen Fletcher?"

"He was sitting out there on the front steps around lunch time," said Linda.

"You haven't seen him since?" asked Jill.

"I haven't looked for him," said Linda.

Jill went outside to look around. She ran into her friend Gwen.

"Hey," she said, "I can't find Fletcher."

"What do you mean?" asked Gwen. "Your dog never needs finding. He never goes anywhere."

"That's just the point," said Jill. "He wasn't in front of the house when I got home."

Fletcher was not the kind of dog to run away. In fact, Fletcher hardly ever moved at all. Every day when Jill came home, Fletcher got up off the front steps and wagged his tail. This was exercise to Fletcher.

"Maybe something strange is going on," said Gwen.

"Do you think somebody snatched Fletcher?" She began to tap the braces on her teeth.

"Don't be silly," said Jill. "What would somebody want Fletcher for?"

"I don't know, but it seems weird to me."

"Look, I know you love mysteries, but that doesn't help me find Fletcher."

"We'll get to the bottom of this . . . I'll help you," said Gwen.

"STOP TAPPING AND DO SOMETHING!" shouted Jill.

All afternoon Gwen and Jill searched for Fletcher.

By nighttime Jill was really worried. When her mother came home from work, Jill told her that Fletcher was missing. Suddenly Jill started to cry.

"It'll be all right," said her mother. "A dog like Fletcher can't go far. I'll call the police."

The police said that nobody had called in about a funny-looking dog with a big stomach.

At school the next day Gwen asked Jill if there was any news.

"He's been gone all night," said Jill. "He never came home."

During math class Jill got the feeling that Fletcher was home safe. She was sure of it.

As soon as school was over Jill and Gwen ran to Jill's house. Fletcher wasn't there.

"The police are not going to find Fletcher," said Gwen. "They don't even know him. We have to make a house-to-house search and ask if anybody has seen him."

"Not everybody knows what Fletcher looks like," said Jill.

"You're right!" said Gwen. "Get some paper and crayons."

Jill and Gwen each made drawings of Fletcher. Then they were ready to begin the search.

The first house they came to was the Hollanders'.

"It's an awfully cute little drawing," said Mr. Hollander. "Which of you girls did it?"

"I did," said Jill. "But have you seen Fletcher?"

"How long has he been missing?" asked Mr. Hollander.

"Since yesterday," said Gwen.

"Well don't worry. My dog goes away for days. But he comes back."

As soon as he closed the door Gwen said, "Why was he in such a hurry to tell us that his dog runs away all the time?"

"Because he does," said Jill. "He's that huge German shepherd."

"I think that man's hiding something," said Gwen.

At the next house they showed Mrs. Duga the picture. "How pretty!!"

"Thank you," said Jill. "Have you seen him by any chance?"

"Now let's see," said Mrs. Duga, "I saw him a few days ago sitting on your front steps."

"But have you seen him since yesterday?" asked Gwen.

"I don't think so," said Mrs. Duga. "Would you girls like a cookie?"

As they walked away Gwen couldn't play with her braces because she was eating. But she said, "Mrs. Duga went out of her way to tell us she saw Fletcher a couple of days ago—WHY?"

"Oh, stop talking with your mouth full," said Jill, talking with her mouth full.

It went on that way all day. Every place they went Gwen found something that seemed not quite right. The one thing Gwen could not find was Fletcher.

Late in the afternoon, they came to a big house that belonged to Fiedler Fernbach. Mr. Fernbach was the most famous person in the neighborhood. He made television commercials.

Mr. Fernbach himself opened the door. "Hi, there," he said. "What can I do for you nice little girls?"

"My name is Jill and this is Gwen," said Jill. "My dog is lost and we're asking everybody if they've seen him."

"NOPE!" said Mr. Fernbach. "Never saw him in my life!"

He started to close the door. . . .

"But Mr. Fernbach," said Gwen, sticking her foot in the door, "you don't even know what he looks like."

"Well . . . er . . . heh, heh . . ." said Mr. Fernbach, turning pink.

"Here's a picture," said Jill.

"Oh," said Mr. Fernbach, hardly looking at the picture. "Just as I thought, I haven't seen him."

He shut the door with a BANG!

"Now this time I'm sure," said Gwen, limping. "It's as plain as Fletcher's nose when Fletcher was around."

"Thanks," said Jill. "That cheers me up."

"I bet he's stolen Fletcher. He thought he'd gotten away with it. . . . Then we showed up. We'll get him."

"You're crazy," said Jill.

"No, I'm not! Fiedler Fernbach filched Fletcher," yelled Gwen, running up the hill.

"Bet you can't say that again," said Jill, catching up to her.

"FIEDLER   FERNBACH   FILCHED   FLETCHER!"
(FASTER)
"FIEDLER   FERNBACH   FILCHED   FLETCHER!"
"FIEDLER   FERNBACH   FILCHED   FLETCHER!"

"HEY!" yelled Gwen. "You know what?"

"What?" asked Jill, puffing.

"Fernbach did do something weird. He said he'd never seen Fletcher *before* he looked at our picture."

"So?" panted Jill.

"How could he say he'd never seen Fletcher if he didn't know what Fletcher looked like?"

Jill stared at Gwen. "You know," she said. "You really *have* something!"

"See!" said Gwen. "SOMETHING STRANGE IS GOING ON!"

"Fernbach could only know what Fletcher looks like if he *has* Fletcher," said Jill. "But what would Fernbach want Fletcher for?"

"That's what we've got to find out," said Gwen. "We've got to go back and watch his every move!"

"It's getting dark," said Jill. "My mother will be worried."

"Well, all right, let's meet in the morning and follow him."

"How?" asked Jill. "He'll go to work in his car. Besides, we've got to go to school."

Gwen played with her braces. It was a problem. Finally she said, "Your mother's O.K. . . . isn't she?"

"Yeah, she's O.K.," said Jill.

"Well, we need her," said Gwen.

Gwen and Jill told Jill's mother everything.

"Let me get this straight," said Jill's mother. "Fernbach said he had never seen Fletcher before he even looked at the drawing, and Fernbach slammed the door on you?"

Gwen and Jill nodded their heads.

"Now, you want me to skip work tomorrow and follow Fernbach?" asked Jill's mother.

"We want to go with you," said Jill. "You also have to write a note to get us out of school."

"Well," said Jill's mother, "I don't know what I'll tell my boss, and I'll look silly if Fernbach catches me— but I'll do it."

The next morning, they got up very early. They drove to Fernbach's house and sat where they were hidden by a big tree.

"Well, here we are," said Jill's mother.

Jill didn't know why, but she wished she had gone to school and never mentioned Fernbach to her mother.

Gwen was too excited to talk.

The garage door went up.

Jill's mother started her car as quietly as she could. When Fernbach moved . . . she was ready.

Jill's mother almost lost Fernbach at a stoplight — she gunned the motor and caught up.

Fernbach stopped in front of a big building.

"He's just going to work," said Jill. "The whole thing's a joke."

"Come on," said Jill's mother. "We're going to get to the bottom of this."

Inside, a woman at the desk asked, "Can I help you?"

"These children are here to see the soap commercial," said Jill's mother.

"Go right in," said the woman, pointing to a big door marked PRIVATE.

As they tiptoed in, they saw Fernbach go through a door at the end of the hall. (Luckily — Fernbach did not see them.)

"Let's go," whispered Gwen.

"Do you think Fletcher's in there?" whispered Jill's mother.

"I thought you were the one who was sure," Jill whispered back.

"We're going in there," said Gwen. "It's now or NEVER!"

Gwen opened the door!

It was a big room, full of movie equipment and bright lights. In the middle, with a big can of dog food by his side, lay Fletcher.

"HOW DARE YOU COME IN IN THE MIDDLE OF SHOOTING!" shouted Fernbach.

Jill ran to Fletcher, who got up and wagged his tail.

"That's the first time I've seen that dog move!" said a man with a camera.

"YOU STOLE JILL'S DOG!" yelled Gwen, pointing at Fernbach.

Fernbach got red in the face. "I just borrowed him."

"You can't borrow a dog without asking," said Jill.

"I saw him on the street," Fernbach answered. "He got up and followed me, and I didn't know whose dog he was."

"That's not true!" said Gwen.

"Yeah," said Jill. "Fletcher didn't follow you 'cause he never follows anyone. You'd be the last person he'd follow."

"Mr. Fernbach," said Jill's mother, "I don't think you're telling the truth. Jill and Gwen are right. You took Fletcher, and I want to know why."

"I'll tell you why," said the man with the camera. "Your dog is a natural for TV. I've never seen a dog lie so still. Besides he's got a nice smile. Fernbach would have had to pay you a lot of money to use your dog. That's why he took him."

"That's right, lady," said another man. "Boy, oh, boy . . . stingy Fernbach."

Fiedler Fernbach looked as if he wanted to cry.

"You're a dog napper!" said Gwen.

"Please don't call the police," Fernbach whined. "I'll pay you the money. Your dog is really perfect for this commercial. He'll be famous."

Gwen and Jill and her mother went into a corner.

"I think Fernbach's going to cry," said Jill, looking over her shoulder.

"I don't know whether we can prove that Fletcher didn't follow him," said Jill's mother. "I'm not sure the police can do anything."

"Maybe you should let Fernbach do the commercial and make him pay you," said Gwen.

"I wouldn't want to make Fletcher a star, but maybe one commercial . . ." said Jill's mother.

"I really don't want to see Fernbach cry," said Jill.

"Well, do we agree?" asked Jill's mother. "We'll let him do this one commercial."

"And TAKE THE MONEY!" said Gwen.

Jill's mother told Fernbach that they had decided not to call the police.

"Oh, thank you! THANK YOU! I know you'll love the way he looks in the commercial!" said Fernbach, trembling with relief.

The day the commercial was on TV, Jill and her mother took part of the money Fletcher had earned and gave a big party.

Fletcher paid for everything. All through the party, he lay on the front steps smiling.

Except when the commercial was on . . .

. . . at that moment Fletcher was asleep.

—Elizabeth Levy

What Do You Think?

1. How would you feel if you came home from school one day and your dog was missing? What would you do about it?

2. Why did Jill agree to let Fletcher make one television commercial?

3. Do you think Jill and Gwen are super sleuths? Tell why.

Taking A Closer Look

1. How did Jill know Fletcher had not run away?

2. Why did Jill have to wait until nighttime to tell her mother about Fletcher?

3. What plan did Jill have for finding Fletcher?

4. Why was Gwen suspicious of Mr. Hollander? Mrs. Duga? Mr. Fernbach? Which one gave Gwen *real* reason to be suspicious?

5. Why was Mr. Fernbach famous in his neighborhood?

6. How did Jill and Gwen find the way to the studio?

7. Where was Fletcher when the girls found him?

8. Why did Mr. Fernbach choose Fletcher for the television commercial?

9. Why didn't Jill's mother report Mr. Fernbach to the police?

Signs, Symbols, and Codes

You speak, write a letter, make a phone call. Your words carry a message. But you pat your dog and your hand carries a message without words. Your dog "replies" with a wagging tail! You too communicate without words. Messages are all around you. You receive messages from bus signs, traffic lights, picture signs, and hundreds of other objects. This unit is filled with signs, symbols, and codes—some old, some new. Read and get the message!

139

Words are fun: "Surprise!"
Words are scary: "Fire!" Words
are friendly: "Hi!" But words are
only one way to communicate.
To signal the bus driver to let
you off, you pull a cord. To let a
friend know you are at the door,
you ring the doorbell. When
drivers want to know where to
turn off a highway, they look for
arrows or light signals for the
"message." Now you follow
this message.

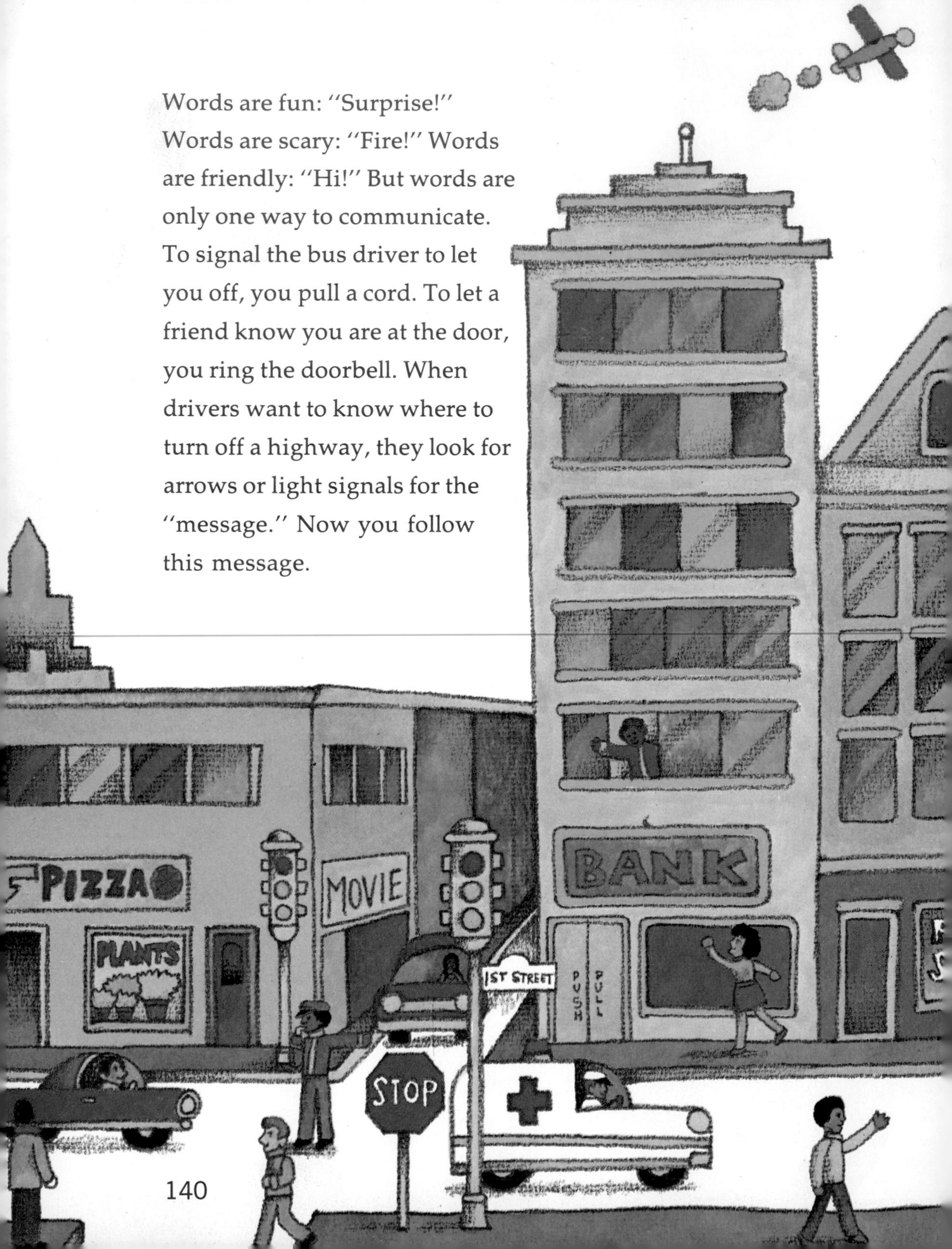

PIZZA

PLANTS

MOVIE

BANK

PUSH PULL

1ST STREET

STOP

COMMUNICATION: JUST WORDS?

Let's Find Out About Communications

We communicate all the time—every day of our lives. Most of the time we communicate by talking. We put our thoughts and ideas into words. Other people understand and use these same words.

Think of all the millions of words that are spoken in your town or city alone, on a single day . . . in your home, in offices, in stores, in restaurants, in your classroom, on the streets. Words, words, words. Everyone has ideas and information to share.

Sometimes it takes too long to share information with a lot of words. That is why we have signs and symbols. They tell a lot of people the same things at the same time.

The ambulance siren tells you that someone has been hurt and you must get out of the way quickly. Red traffic lights tell you to STOP: traffic is moving in the other direction. A flag at half-mast tells you that someone important has died. Painted signs tell you the names of shops, and often what they sell. Signs on doors tell you whether to PULL or PUSH and where to go in and out.

People can also communicate with one another quickly without uttering a word. Just by raising your hand, you can let your teacher know that you want to say something or ask or answer a question. By putting your finger to your lips, you can warn someone to be quiet. By waving your arm, you can signal a friendly "hello" to someone across the street.

Feelings are sometimes hard to put into words. People often communicate their feelings by the look on their faces. You can smile . . . frown . . . laugh. There is a whole theater in your face and in all the faces around you. In people's faces you can see their feelings acted out.

The way people sit and walk and use their hands tells about their feelings, too. If you are bored, you may slump in a chair or yawn or drum your fingers on the table. If you are excited about a birthday party or a trip to the circus, you may rush around jumping and skipping and smiling at everyone. If you are in a bad mood, you may kick a stone on your way home from school, and glare at everybody. You can often tell how people feel just by looking at them.

People can communicate also through the things they create. Artists can communicate many different things in paintings and drawings. One painting can tell about summer and how cool it feels to lie in a hammock under the trees. Other paintings can tell other things.

Composers can communicate all sorts of ideas and feelings through music. One piece of music may sound like waves crashing against the shore; another may sound like soldiers marching to battle. Music can make a listener feel happy or sad or ready to rush off and do great things.

Authors can write books to tell about all the wonderful things in the world . . . elephants and mountains, violets and lollipops. In their books, authors can also tell about people and their feelings. Books can show us that we all feel the same things, no matter who we are or where we live.

Things like paintings and music and books help us to communicate with one another. So do magazines, newspapers, television and radio, and movies. They all help us to find out what is going on in the world and in other people's minds.

—*Valerie Pitt*

Let's Begin at the Beginning

People did not always have our wonderful ways of communicating. But they did find other ways of communicating with each other. Long ago, people learned to speak, perhaps by making sounds they heard around them. They may have made the buzzing sound of a bee, the bark of a dog, and the gurgle of a brook.

These early people were also the first to learn to write. They did it by drawing pictures on the walls of caves.

Years later, the American Indians used signs as well as words to communicate. They also drew pictures to tell others their thoughts. The pictures were drawn on animal skins, shells, and wood.

The Indians also used fire and smoke to send messages. This kind of message is called a signal. The sender built a bonfire and then partly covered it with wet grass to make more smoke rise from it. Big and little puffs meant certain things. Each village had its own smoke signals.

The Egyptians were the first to work out an alphabet. Their writing was made up of long rows of signs. They drew signs for such words as sun, moon, stars, kings, and gods. Later on, they made simple marks instead of signs. The marks became an alphabet.

At first they wrote with sticks on wet clay bricks. The bricks were dried in the sun and called tablets. Some tablets have lasted for thousands of years and can be seen today in many museums.

The Egyptians also wrote on sheets made from papyrus—a plant that grew in the Nile River. The sheets were made from strips cut from the stems of the plants. They pasted the sheets together and rolled each end on a stick. These rolls of papyrus sheets were called scrolls.

Long ago the Chinese also made paper and did printing. They may have learned how to make paper by watching wasps chew wood into pulp for their nests. In order to print, the Chinese cut words and pictures on blocks of wood. Then they dipped the blocks into dyes and pressed the blocks onto paper.

Learning to read and write helped people to have much better lives. As they learned more, they needed ways of sending messages.

Some villages built stone towers and made fires on top to signal other villages about an enemy. Huge logs were burned near the seashores to warn ships of danger. These burning logs were the first lighthouses. Today, lighthouses use electricity to flash signals to ships.

In central Africa people used drums to communicate with one another. A drummer from one village would beat out a message for his tribe in a second village. Someone in the second village would beat out the same message for the people in the village beyond. Members of the same tribe understood the pattern of the drum beats, but strangers did not. By using this "jungle telegraph," as it was often called, drummers could send an important message safely for hundreds of miles.

Bells were also used to send messages in early times. Church bells were rung to call people together when there was important news. In some towns a man walked along the streets and called out the news. He rang a bell to get the people to come outdoors and listen. He was called the Town Crier.

In early times, letters were often hand-delivered by travelers. Later, Post Riders, messengers on horseback, became the first regular mail carriers.

In order that letters could go more swiftly, the Pony Express was begun on the American frontier. A man rode horseback with the mail fastened to the saddle. About every ten miles he changed horses. After he had ridden a hundred miles, another man took the mail and rode on. In that way the mail was carried from place to place. After better roads were built, letters were sent by stagecoach. It took many weeks for the coach to travel a few hundred miles.

Now, mail is delivered every day. Sometimes it travels hundreds of miles on fast trains overnight. Usually it is sent on airplanes. Letters and packages can be delivered to people across the ocean in three or four days.

Newspapers are important for communications too. The first papers ever printed were small—only two or four pages, and were printed once a week.

Today, there are millions of newspapers printed every hour all over the world. There are also many books and magazines published each year. These give us both information and entertainment.

Next to talking with people face to face, we use the telephone most often. In most places today we get the number we want by dialing. We can even dial a number in a city far away. We can also talk by telephone to someone on a train, ship, or in another country.

We would not have the telephone, telegraph, radio, or television if no one had learned to use electricity. The telephone, the telegraph, the radio, and the television all use electricity and help us communicate.

The first message by telegraph was sent in 1844 by Samuel Morse between Washington, D.C. and Baltimore, Maryland. For many years telegrams were sent by Morse Code, a system of dots and dashes tapped on keys of the telegraph set. The message traveled by electricity over a wire. Only one message could be sent at a time.

Now a person does not need to tap the code on a set. Instead the message can be typed on a Teleprinter. Between many large cities 2000 telegrams can be sent at one time by radio beam. We no longer need to use wires. Radio towers carry the beam.

It took many years of work to find a way to send messages by using the air waves instead of wires. Then, it took more years of work by many people to give us radio.

From their work with radio, scientists were later able to give us television. They learned how to send pictures as well as sound through the air waves. Tall towers were built to catch the waves and send them on to the next tower, and then on into our homes.

Radio and television let us hear and see news from all parts of the world. They bring us weather reports, warn us of danger, and give us pleasant entertainment. Boats and police cars have two-way radios; they can both send and receive messages.

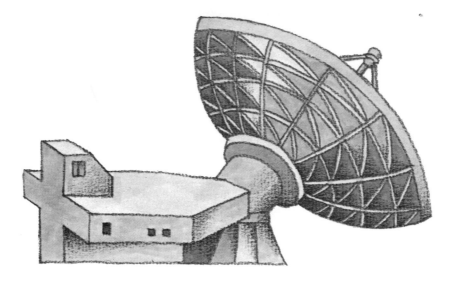

From the beginning of time people have worked to make life more pleasant. And now, the Space Age is bringing wonders never even imagined fifty years ago. Two-way telephone conversations have been held by the use of earth's natural satellite, the moon. Telephone calls through space have been made by the use of satellites. Recorded messages have been sent by radio beam to these satellites and bounced back to a receiving station.

Scientists believe that satellites in space will make new and better ways of communicating possible. No one knows yet what marvels will be brought about in the future.

—*Mary E. Nelson*

What Do You Think?

1. Before the telephone, radio, and television were invented, how different do you think people's lives were from yours?

2. Tell some ways in which your life is better because an alphabet has been created.

3. Can you think of any ways that picture writing tells more than word writing? Tell about them.

Taking A Closer Look

1. What are three examples given to show how people can communicate without speaking a word? What others can you think of?

2. How do people who create—artists, authors, musicians, dancers—share their thoughts and feelings with others?

3. Tell about the first mail carriers. What changes have taken place in the delivery of mail since the days of those first mail carriers?

4. What are the two most common means of communication that most people use today? Why do you think people use these two most often?

Last year you grew ___ inches. Yesterday the temperature rose to ___ degrees. On your next birthday you will be ___ years old. After you spent ___ of your birthday money, you had only ___ left. How can you fill in these blanks? You'll use *numbers*, of course. Do you know how people first made numerals? How they added and subtracted? You don't need to guess. But get ready for some surprises.

Speaking of Numbers

A Language Everyone Knows

There is one language we all speak, no matter which country we live in . . . the language of numbers!

The numbers we use are the same ones used by people in countries all over the world. Other countries may have other words for numbers. But they all mean the same. Wherever you travel you will find everyone speaking the same language . . . numbers.

Without language you can't say "Hello" or "Thank you." Without numbers you can't tell what time it is . . . what your address or telephone number is . . . how much things cost . . . or how old you are. Without numbers you can't even count or tell how many of something you want.

Without numbers grown-ups couldn't cook food properly . . . buy at the market as they do now . . . know how fast their car is going and on what road. They wouldn't know the right change if they couldn't count. They wouldn't know how much money to spend and how much to save. Or how much to give you for an allowance!

153

As much as children and grown-ups in general need numbers, scientists need them even more. Scientists use numbers to solve problems. They learn new things about the world this way. The more they learn about the world, the better we can make it.

Sometimes, when scientists solve problems with numbers, they find numbers help them invent new things. They may invent television . . . a cure for a disease . . . a better washing machine . . . a way to get oil from under the earth . . . a new plastic . . . a strong metal. Or they may invent a faster rocket . . . a more powerful fuel . . . a better way to guide a rocket to the moon. When our space ships blast off for other planets scientists know exactly where they're going . . . thanks to numbers.

These scientists are astronomers. They have never been to the moon or Mars. But they know how far away the planets are. They have figured it out with numbers.

It may seem like magic to you. Yet scientists use the same numbers you do.

The language of numbers is called MATHEMATICS. You are learning it in school now. The simplest kind is called ARITHMETIC. In high school and college you will learn other kinds of mathematics.

To help all of us with mathematics, machines have been invented. They let us do problems faster and with fewer mistakes.

We know that the abacus or counting board was the first of these machines. It was invented many thousands of years ago, but it is still being used in China, Japan, and other countries.

Today, COMPUTERS are used all over the world. These computers seem to think. Of course they really don't. They do only what people tell them to do. But they do it much faster than a person could.

Inside, a computer may look very confusing to you. But the people who run it know just what to do. They can make a computer store up facts and give them to other people. They can make it solve hard problems and help us to live better.

Like people all over the world, these machines speak the same language . . . numbers.

—*Leslie Waller*

Numerals Are In

To work with numbers, we need numerals. Long before the Romans were using letters like **I, II, III** to express number ideas, people in India, called Hindus, were writing numerals. They looked like this:

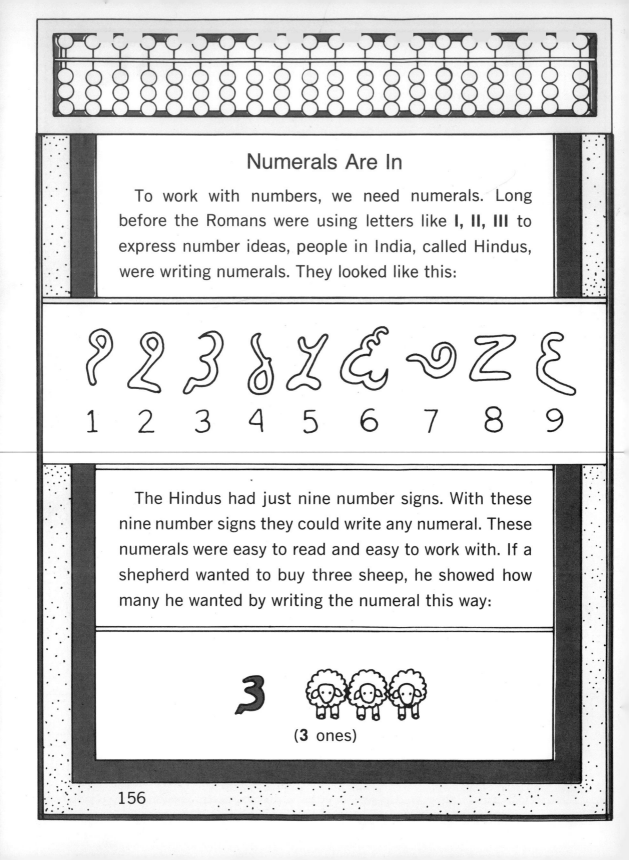

The Hindus had just nine number signs. With these nine number signs they could write any numeral. These numerals were easy to read and easy to work with. If a shepherd wanted to buy three sheep, he showed how many he wanted by writing the numeral this way:

(**3** ones)

If he wanted to buy thirty-three sheep, he wrote the numeral this way:

33

(**3** tens and **3** ones)

Each three had a "place value."

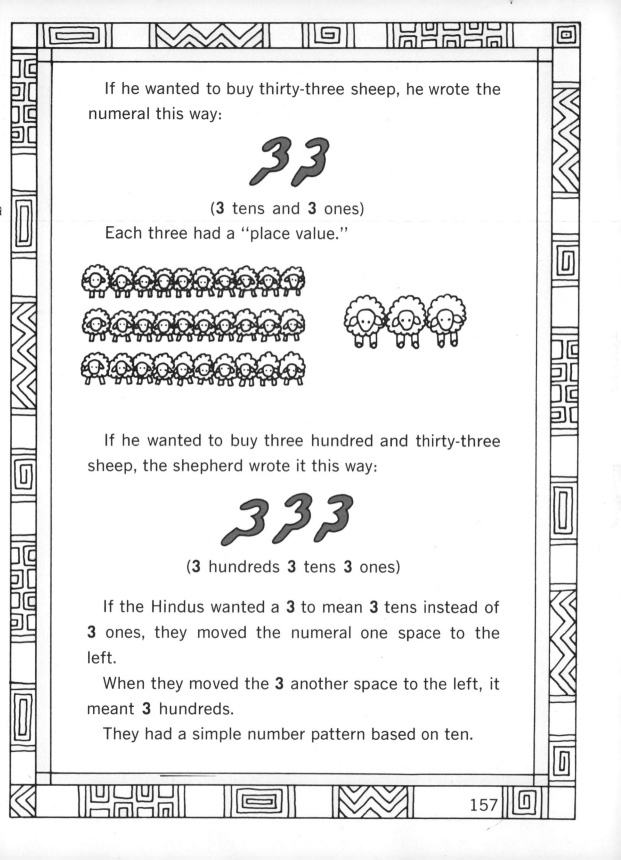

If he wanted to buy three hundred and thirty-three sheep, the shepherd wrote it this way:

333

(**3** hundreds **3** tens **3** ones)

If the Hindus wanted a **3** to mean **3** tens instead of **3** ones, they moved the numeral one space to the left.

When they moved the **3** another space to the left, it meant **3** hundreds.

They had a simple number pattern based on ten.

How could people write three hundred and three when they had no number sign for tens? They just left a space and wrote it this way:

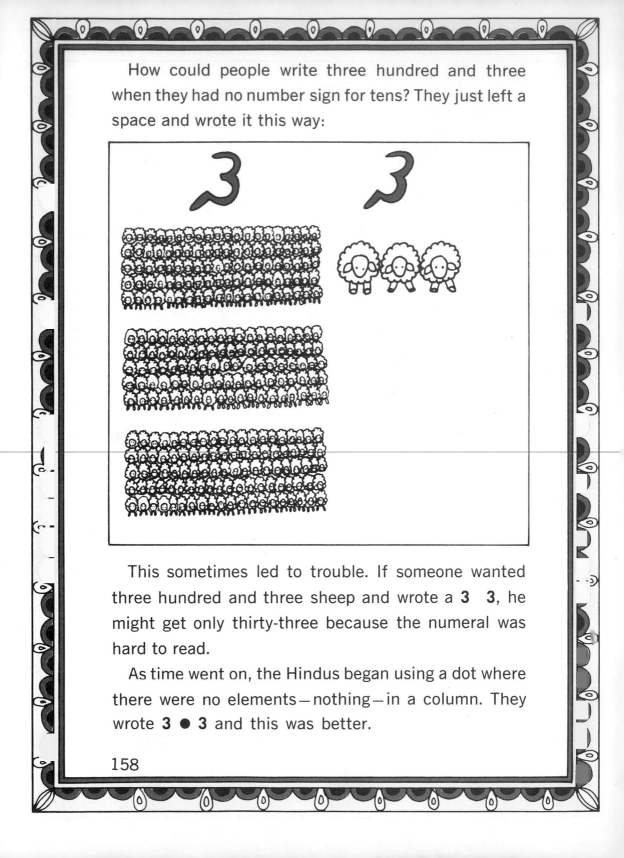

This sometimes led to trouble. If someone wanted three hundred and three sheep and wrote a **3   3**, he might get only thirty-three because the numeral was hard to read.

As time went on, the Hindus began using a dot where there were no elements—nothing—in a column. They wrote **3 ● 3** and this was better.

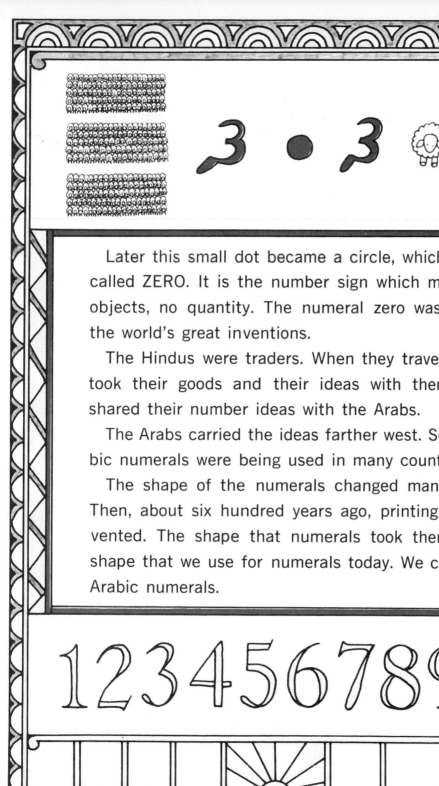

Later this small dot became a circle, which is now called ZERO. It is the number sign which means no objects, no quantity. The numeral zero was one of the world's great inventions.

The Hindus were traders. When they traveled they took their goods and their ideas with them. They shared their number ideas with the Arabs.

The Arabs carried the ideas farther west. Soon Arabic numerals were being used in many countries.

The shape of the numerals changed many times. Then, about six hundred years ago, printing was invented. The shape that numerals took then is the shape that we use for numerals today. We call them Arabic numerals.

1234567890

Working with Numbers

Long ago people found a way to work with numbers without using any numerals, or number signs. They worked with an abacus. The word abacus comes from the Latin word *abax* which means tablet.

The early abacus was made by drawing three lines in the sand. Pebbles were placed in the lines. The pebbles can show six hundred and thirty-seven when placed this way.

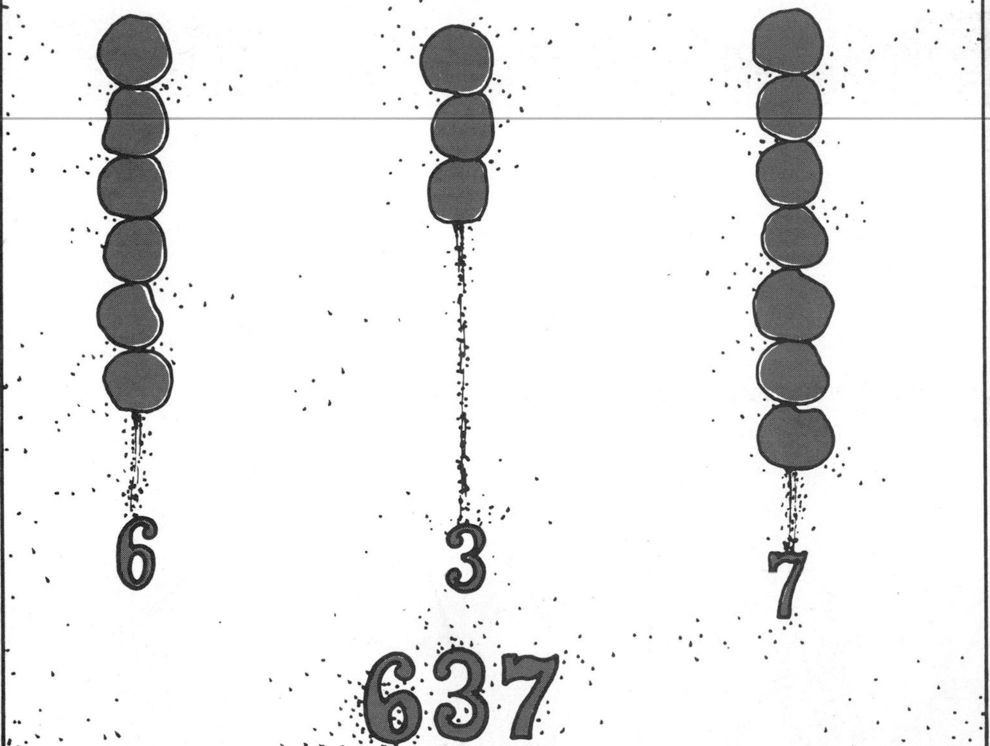

6   3   7

637

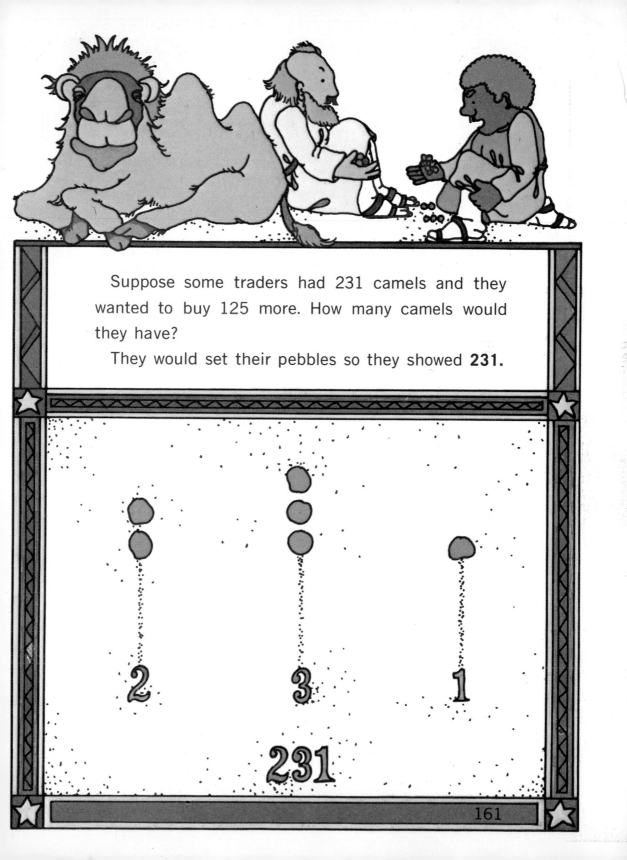

Suppose some traders had 231 camels and they wanted to buy 125 more. How many camels would they have?

They would set their pebbles so they showed **231**.

2

3

1

231

Then they would put five pebbles on the line for ones and two pebbles on the line for tens. On the line for hundreds they would put one pebble.

3

5

6

356

Then they could see that they would have 356 camels.

If 356 camels were more camels than the traders could use, they might sell 45 of them. How many would they have left?

To find out, they probably took five pebbles from the line for ones and four pebbles from the line for tens. They could see then that they had 311 camels left.

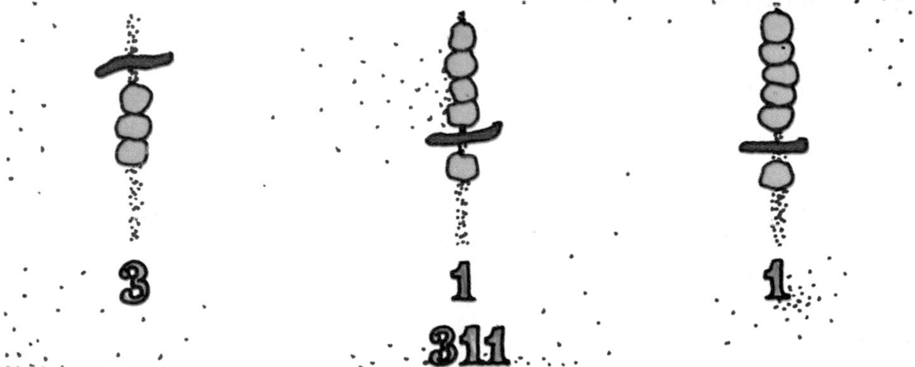

3   1   1

311

The Chinese used an abacus with rows of colored beads. The beads could be moved back and forth on rods. Even today, some people use an abacus when they are working with numbers.

Numbers are handy and help us save time.

We use numbers every day. They tell us how far, how fast, how much, how many, how tall.

We work with numbers every day . . . if we bake a cake . . . play a game . . . keep a score.

Engineers work with numbers when they build a bridge . . . or design a jet . . . or find the height of a mountain on the moon by measuring its shadow.

The idea of numbers goes on and on and on, without end.

—*Philip Carona*

What Do You Think?

1. How does the system of numbers make your life simpler and more pleasant?

2. What are some of the ways you use numbers almost every day? What problems would you have on a "typical day" if you did not have a system of numbers?

3. How are numbers used in sports? Do you think these games would be more or less interesting without numbers? Why?

Taking A Closer Look

1. Who created the first numerals? How do they compare with the numerals we use today?

2. How did zero come to be used in mathematics?

3. Why were the Hindus so much interested in numbers? How did the Arabs learn about numbers?

4. What was the first "number machine"? How did it operate? What machines help make mathematics easier today?

5. Scientists use numbers in many ways. What type of scientists were especially helpful to the space program? How did they help get to the moon?

Picture signs deliver a short, quick message. Walk through a shopping district and see for yourself. A steer's head appears on one sign. The message? A butcher's shop or a meat market, what else? See that large boot outside another shop. The message? That's right—a shoe store. Now begin your tour through the next few pages. Everywhere —picture signs and symbols. . . . What's *their* message?

Communicating with Picture Signs and Symbols

Numbers have their own special signs, but there are many other kinds of signs. Take a ride into town and this is what you will see:

Signs. Signs. Everywhere.

All kinds of signs.

All those signs have words, but there's another kind of sign without words. It's a picture sign. It tells you something without spelling it out in letters. A clock-face is a picture sign. It tells you the time. A traffic signal is also a sign without words. Green says "GO"; Yellow says "WAIT"; Red means "STOP."

Here's a different kind of picture:

It's the sign on a mailbox. We call it a symbol, which means that it stands for something else. The eagle is a symbol of the United States and the eagle sign tells you where to find a U.S. mailbox.

Once you start looking around, you begin to see many signs without words.

Signs That Lead the Way

Everyone knows what arrow signs mean. You see them everywhere, in all kinds of shapes and sizes. And everywhere in the world they mean the same thing. Even people who can't read can understand an arrow. It's a useful sign. It gives you quick, simple directions such as "TURN RIGHT," "GO AROUND THE BEND," "TURN LEFT."

Now let's see how we can use the arrow sign, together with another picture, to show people how to find something without saying it in words. Let's pretend we are visiting a zoo in a foreign country.

In a zoo in Greece we might see this sign:

It says: "To the Monkeys." But it doesn't mean a thing to someone who can't read Greek.

Here's the same sign in pictures:

In any language these signs say: "This way to the Birds" . . . "To the Crocodiles" . . . "To the Bears."

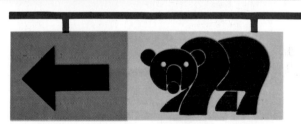

And when you're ready to leave the zoo, here's a picture sign that tells you where to get the bus.

Picture Signs That Tell a Story

American Indians used picture signs long before white men came here. They knew how to tell a whole story in picture signs.

Here is a sentence in English, followed by the picture signs an Indian might have used to write the same sentence:

"At sunrise three men left the camp
beside the lake to hunt deer, because
they were hungry."

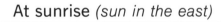

At sunrise *(sun in the east)*

three men

left the camp *(footsteps going away from wigwams)*

beside the lake *(stream going in and out of lake)*

to hunt *(with an arrow)*

deer *(which have antlers)*

because they were hungry. *(line across stomach to show it is empty)*

Here are three picture sign messages left by an Indian who lived alone in Maine many years ago. He scratched these messages on birch bark. Then he rolled it up and tied it to his wigwam so that his friends would know where he had gone.

This means: "I am going across the lake to hunt deer."

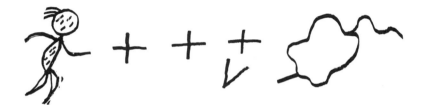

This says: "I am going toward the lake, but will turn where there is a pointer before reaching the lake."

The third message means: "I am going hunting and will be gone all winter." This is shown by the sled and the snowshoes.

The Indians of Alaska also used picture signs to tell a story. They carved tiny figures on pieces of ivory or wood.

Here is a drawing of a picture carving in which an Indian tells the story of a hunt. It shows him leaving his house and then tells how many animals he caught. All the animals he caught have their heads pointing to his house. The ones he did not catch are facing away from the house. He caught one wolf, two deer, and three beavers. The ones that got away were a porcupine, a seal, and a fox.

Flags Are Symbols Too

If you are going out on the ocean in a boat and you see a triangular red flag it is telling you that strong winds are beginning to blow — up to 38 miles an hour.

If you see two triangular red flags on the same stick it means the winds are even stronger — up to 54 miles an hour — and you'd better stay on shore.

When you see a square red flag flying from a boat, it means the boat is in trouble and needs help. A similar red flag at the end of a truck means "DANGER. STAY AWAY." And on a skating rink it means "DANGER. THIN ICE."

And, of course, this flag is also a sign. It's the sign of the United States. The 50 white stars on blue stand for the 50 states, and the 13 red and white stripes stand for the 13 original colonies.

Each independent country in the world now has a flag of its own. It wasn't always that way. Flags did not begin to be popular until about 1,400 years ago.

173

These colorful emblems were almost always signs of war. In ancient times soldiers wore armor in battle and they all looked very much alike. In order to recognize one side from the other each side carried a different flag. Often each knight had his own special flag which helped to identify him and his men during battle.

When modern nations began to develop about 600 years ago, the many separate flags disappeared. Instead, each country chose one flag for all its people. Today there are more than 150 national flags in the world. There is a story and a reason behind each one of these, as there is behind the U.S. flag.

Canada

When Canada became independent of England in 1964, the Canadian government chose this flag because the maple leaf is the national symbol of Canada. Before they decided on it they looked at 4,000 other designs.

Japan

The white flag of Japan has a red circle that stands for the sun. It is the ancient Japanese symbol for the Sun Goddess who is said to have created the island of Japan.

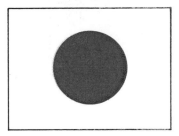

United Nations

The United Nations flag is blue and white. It shows a map of the world and two olive branches, an ancient peace symbol. Peace among the nations of the world is the hope of all people everywhere.

Symbols Tell about Customs

Each country has its own holiday symbols. In the United States we have a Liberty Bell for July 4, a turkey for Thanksgiving Day, a cherry branch and hatchet for Washington's Birthday, and a log cabin for Lincoln's Birthday.

In China the sign of the new year is a huge paper dragon which is carried in parades with thousands of colored lanterns.

And in Sweden the winter festival is St. Lucia's Day when young girls in white dresses and red sashes wear crowns of lighted candles and sing for grownups at parties all over the land.

Signs like these are used in festivals all over the world. They tell us something interesting about the customs of these lands.

Signs and symbols can tell us a lot, but they cannot take the place of words altogether. With words we can express ideas and thoughts. We can't do that very well with picture signs and symbols.

If we want to find out about history, or write poetry, or tell other people what we are thinking and feeling, then we need words and language. And not only our own language but also the languages of other countries.

No, signs and symbols alone will not give us an international language, but they can point the way.

—Winifred and Cecil Lubell

What Do You Think?

1. Tell how some picture signs you have seen today have helped you.

2. Put yourself in a situation where you might *have* to depend on picture signs or symbols. Tell about it.

3. In what ways is the language of words usually the most useful way of communicating? Think about both written and spoken language.

Taking A Closer Look

1. When do people find picture signs and symbols more useful than words?

2. What do the picture sign messages found in Maine tell about the Indians who left them?

3. Why were the first flags made? How are flags used today?

4. Why are flags especially useful as symbols on boats?

5. What does the flag of the United Nations tell about the organization it represents?

6. Explain the meaning of two or three national or holiday symbols of the United States that you particularly like.

Secrets are old. And secrets are fun. Keeping secrets *secret* is the most fun of all. How can you do it? One *sure* way is to use a code. Whether you write in symbols or speak a language you and a friend invent, the *secret* is what counts. Enter the following pages on tiptoe. Turn the pages quietly . . . discover the mystery behind *codes*!

COMMUNICATING WITH CODES

Space Codes

The easiest code messages to make are Space Code messages.

Can you read this?

sendhelpatonce

There are four small words in the message. But there are no spaces between the words. The message is

send help at once

The same message could be written this way,

sendhel patonce

or this way.

sen dhel pato nce

Here are the three secret messages with lines separating the words:

send|hel|p|at|once
send|hel p|at|once
sen d|hel p|at|o nce

Can you think of another way to write the words so that the message is secret? If you do, you can make up your own Space Code.

Here is a harder Space Code message.

dnes pleh ta ecno

Can you read it? The message is

send help at once

This time the words are written backwards. So **d-n-e-s** is really **s-e-n-d**. And **p-l-e-h** is really **h-e-l-p**.

When you write a message in code, you are *en*coding it. Your friend has to *de*code the message to read it. That means your friend has to write it in English.

Here is another Space Code message.

send help at once

The letters look funny, don't they? If you hold the message up to a mirror, you can read it.

There is another way to read mirror writing. Turn the paper over so the message is on the other side. Hold the paper up to a light. You can see through the paper and read the message.

Hidden Words Code

This next secret message is written in pencil and red ink. No one can read it!

aghiti ttetbtBe sdenen

But—if you put a piece of transparent red paper over the message, you can read it!

don't tell the secret

This code is called the Hidden Words Code. The hidden message is written in pencil. The letters in red ink are hiding the secret message.

If you don't have a piece of red cellophane or other transparent red paper, you can make one. To begin with, you will need a piece of tracing paper. Then take a red crayon or a felt-tip pen and color the paper red all over. If you put the red paper over a Hidden Words message, you will not see the red letters. You will see the pencil lines and you can read the message.

Here is how to write a Hidden Words message. First, write the message in pencil. Do not press down too hard with the pencil. The letters must be light gray.

bring the map

Next, add red lines to the pencil words. Use bright-red ink or a red pencil. Try to change the letters into other letters. The word **the** can be hidden by changing the **t** to a **B**; the **h** into a **ti**; and **e** becomes **s**.

This is how **the** looks when it is encoded:

Here is another message for you to decode. Use the red transparent paper.

dɵmle db eigbtt

What if your Hidden Words message was found by an enemy? And what if that person had some red transparent paper and knew how to read the message? What could you do to keep an enemy from reading the message?

The answer: use *two* codes on the message. Here is a message in two codes.

doo Rdttbem dp

The two codes are: (1) the Hidden Words Code, and (2) a Space Code.

Here is how the message looks with the red transparent paper over it.

loo katt hem ap

Now you can read the real letters. Change the spaces and find the real words.

look at the map

Later, you will learn more codes. Try to use two of them in the same message. Using two codes together is a good way to keep a message secret. Be sure your friend knows which two codes you use.

Alphabet Codes

Alphabet Codes are still another interesting kind of code. Here is a secret message in an Alphabet Code.

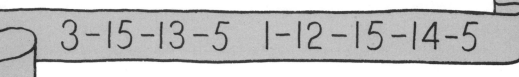

3-15-13-5 1-12-15-14-5

This message is written in the Numbered Alphabet Code. The code card is at the bottom.

The first row of letters is the regular alphabet. The second row are numbers from 1 to 26. There is a number for each letter of the alphabet.

Here is how to decode the first word of the secret message.

Find the number **3** in the code card. The letter above **3** is **c**. Write down the letter **c** on your paper.

The second number is **15**. Find **15** on the code card. The letter **15** is **o**. Write **o** next to **c**. The third number is **13**. The letter above **13** is **m**.

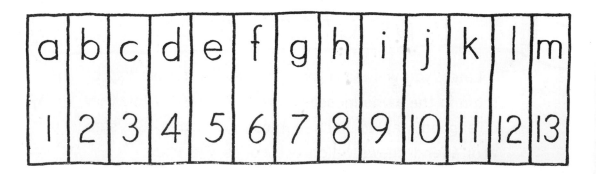

Here is the decoded word so far:

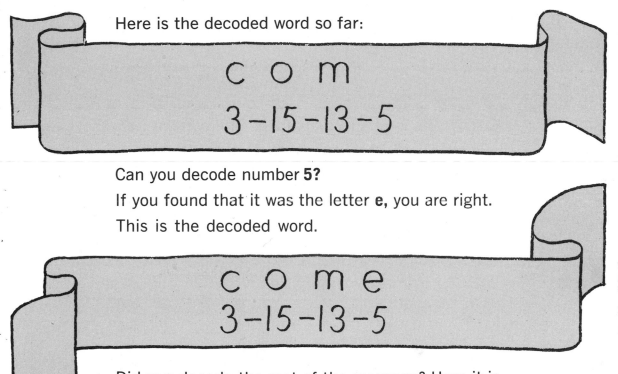

c o m

3 – 15 – 13 – 5

Can you decode number **5?**

If you found that it was the letter **e,** you are right.

This is the decoded word.

c o m e

3 – 15 – 13 – 5

Did you decode the rest of the message? Here it is.

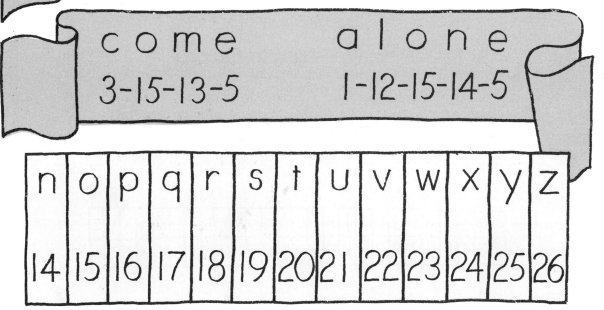

come   alone

3-15-13-5   1-12-15-14-5

n	o	p	q	r	s	t	u	v	w	x	y	z
14	15	16	17	18	19	20	21	22	23	24	25	26

Here is a message for you to write in the Numbered Alphabet Code.

go to the cave

Change the letters into numbers. The number under the letter **g** is **7**. The number under the letter **o** is **15**. The first code word in the message is

go
7–15

Here is the rest of the message written in code.

g   o   t o   t h e   c a v e
7 – 15   20-15   20-8-5   3 – 1-22-5

—*John Peterson*

More Messages to Decode

Now that you know how alphabet codes work, you can change the code easily. The simplest way to do this is to shift the numbers under the regular alpha-bet.

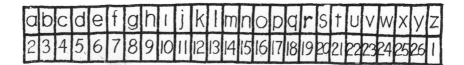

a	b	c	d	e	f	g	h	i	j	k	l	m	n	o	p	q	r	s	t	u	v	w	x	y	z
2	3	4	5	6	7	8	9	10	11	12	13	14	15	16	17	18	19	20	21	22	23	24	25	26	1

Here is a message in **Code 2**. Using another sheet of paper, decode the message.

5·6·4·16·5·10·15·8 10·20 62·20·26 10·7
26·16·22 12·15·16·24 21·9·6 4·16·5·6

You can make other codes by shifting the numbers to the right or to the left under the letters.

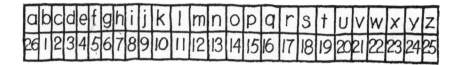

a	b	c	d	e	f	g	h	i	j	k	l	m	n	o	p	q	r	s	t	u	v	w	x	y	z
26	1	2	3	4	5	6	7	8	9	10	11	12	13	14	15	16	17	18	19	20	21	22	23	24	25

Here is a message in **Code 3** for you to decode.

18·4·4 7·14·22 4·26·18·24 8·19 8·18
19·14 12·26·10·4 26 13·4·22 2·14·3·4

You can also make codes using the letters of the alphabet instead of numbers. All you have to do is shift the letters around instead of the numbers.

a	b	c	d	e	f	g	h	i	j	k	l	m	n	o	p	q	r	s	t	u	v	w	x	y	z
b	c	d	e	f	g	h	i	j	k	l	m	n	o	p	q	r	s	t	u	v	w	x	y	z	a

Here is a message in **Code 4**. Decode it.

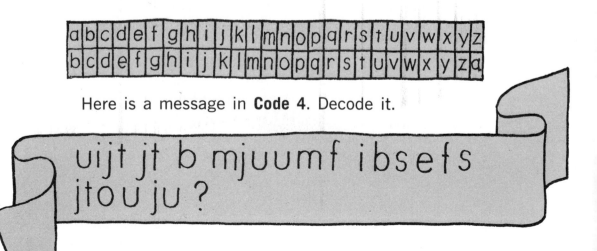

uijt jt b mjuumf ibsefs
jtou ju ?

When you get used to encoding and decoding you can scramble your letters or numbers any way you want to make the code harder.

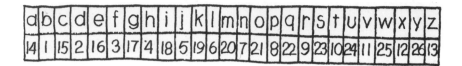

a	b	c	d	e	f	g	h	i	j	k	l	m	n	o	p	q	r	s	t	u	v	w	x	y	z
14	1	15	2	16	3	17	4	18	5	19	6	20	7	21	8	22	9	23	10	24	11	25	12	26	13

Here is a message in **Code 5**: What does it say?

18·3 26·21·24 25·14·7·10 10·21 20·14·19·16

26·21·24·9 15·21·2·16 20·21·9·16

18·7·10·16·9·16·23·10·18·7·17 26·21·24 15·14·7

16·11·16·7 20·18·12 6·16·10·10·16·9·23 14·7·2

7·24·20·1·16·9·23 10·4·14·10 20·14·19·16 18·10

4·14·9·2·16·9 3·21·9 14·7·26·21·7·16 10·21

3·18·7·2 21·24·10 25·4·14·10 10·4·16

15·21·2·16 18·23 24·7·6·16·23·23 26·21·24

10·16·6·6 10·4·16·20

188

What Do You Think?

1. Why do you think codes are so useful?
2. What types of people would find codes especially necessary in their work?
3. How do you think codes might have begun?
4. When would you prefer to write in codes?

Taking A Closer Look

1. Why are messages in Space Code the easiest to write?
2. What is the difference between encoding and decoding? Which do you think is more fun? Why?
3. Explain how you can keep your coded messages from being read by strangers.
4. What equipment will help you decode messages?
5. Choose one type of code and explain the reason for its name.

Mimi's Fingers

I am blind. All that I can see
My enchanted fingers bring to me,
As if all sight were mingled with all touch
I do not mind not-seeing very much.
In Braille I read the words these fingers trace,
And with them come to know your smile, your face,
Your buckled shoes, the silk-thread of your hair,
The fabric of each suit and dress you wear;
All shapes, all sizes, how long, how far, how high,
How round a bowl, how gently curved the sky,
How pointed the far tip-top of a hill,
The narrow table of a window sill.
I know a snowflake as a melting star,
The sticky-thick of honey and of tar.
Color alone my fingers cannot do.
Could you, could you, tell me about blue?

—*Mary O'Neill*

What would you do if you could only make one sound? And suppose that sound had to tell everything you wanted to say? The foghorn wails its warning—with one sound. The fire horn moans its message— with one sound. The ice-cream bell rings its message—with one sound. And the engine? You *know* the engine's one sound—TOOT TOOT. Again and again, TOOT TOOT TOOT. Join the engineer in this story and learn what "engine-talk" is all about!

192

HOW ENGINES TALK

When we hear train whistles, the engine is talking. Engines have a language of their own. Sometimes the engineer is sending a message to another train. Sometimes he is talking to the conductor or the brakeman. Sometimes he is telling people to stay away from the tracks.

Engines talk with short whistles. They talk with long whistles. They talk with long and short whistles together.

People who work on the trains know what the different signals mean. Everyone knows that when the train whistle blows, it means:

"Keep away from the tracks!"

Here is D. F.[1] Engine Number 312.

The workers have tested the motors.

They have filled the engine with water and fuel oil and sand.

They have cleaned the windshields and the head-lights.

Now the engine is ready to go.

[1] D.F. Diesel Fuel

The engineer blows two long blasts on the whistle.
TOOOOT TOOOOT
He is telling the roundhouse men, "I am going to move forward."

Now the engine has moved into the railroad yards.
The engineer blows four short blasts on the whistle.
TOOT TOOT TOOT TOOT
"Where shall I go?"

The switchman waves to the engineer. "Come ahead."
The engineer whistles his answers. TOOT TOOT
"Here I come!"

The train that Engine Number 312 is going to pull is on the first track.
The cars are all ready for the engine to couple onto the first car.
The switchman signals for the engineer to back up.
The engineer answers. TOOT TOOT TOOT
"I will back up."

The engineer whistles now for the air man.

TOOOOT TOOOOT TOOOOT TOOOOT TOOOOT

"Come and couple me up."

Quickly, the engine is coupled and ready to go.

But the engineer must find out if the conductor is ready.

TOOOOOOOOT

"Are we all ready?"

The conductor is on the caboose at the rear end of the train. He is testing the air that runs in a pipe under all the cars.

The engineer looks at the air gauges on the panel in front of the cab of the engine. They tell him the conductor is ready.

Then the engineer blows the whistle.

TOOOOT TOOOOT

195

The train goes very fast.

The speedometer says, "50," as the engine races to a crossing ahead.

The engineer blows the whistle to warn all the people and the automobiles and trucks.

TOOOOT TOOOOT TOOT TOOOOT

He makes it sound like *toot toot t' toot.*

That means, "Stop, Look, and Listen!"

The engineer sees a red signal. He has to stop. There must be something wrong around the hill.

The engineer signals the head brakeman.

TOOT TOOT TOOT TOOOOT

That tells the head brakeman to go ahead around the hill and see what is wrong.

The engineer blows the whistle again.

TOOOOT TOOT TOOT TOOT

That tells the rear brakeman to go back with a red flag and stop any trains coming from behind.

Finally, the signal turns to green and the train can go ahead.

First the engineer must call the rear brakeman so he can get on the caboose.

The engineer blows the whistle.

TOOOOT TOOOOT TOOOOT TOOOOT

"Flagman, come back to the train."

Now Number 312 must climb a high mountain.

The track goes up and up and up.

The engineer has orders to stop at this station and get a helper diesel engine to help his train climb the mountain.

The helper diesel calls, TOOT TOOT TOOT TOOT. He wants to know whether to get behind the train and push or get on the front and pull.

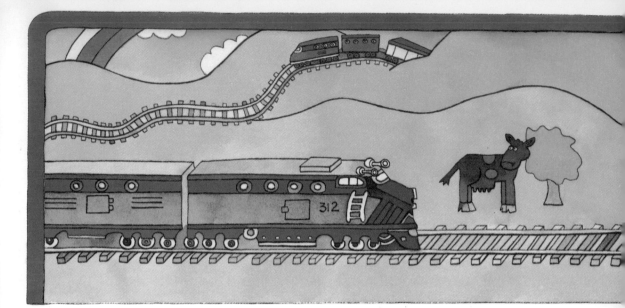

Number 312's engineer blows the whistle.

TOOT TOOT TOOOOT

That means, "Get on the front and take charge."

The helper engine answers. TOOT TOOT TOOOOT

"All right. I'll take charge of the train."

When Number 312 gets to the top of the mountain, it stops.

The engineer blows the whistle.

TOOT TOOT TOOOOT

"I'll take charge of my train again."

The head brakeman hurries to cut off the helper and put it onto a siding to let Number 312 go by.

The engineer sees a cow on the track ahead. He blows the crossing warning.

TOOOOT TOOOOT TOOT TOOOOT

The cow is still on the track.

The engineer blows the alarm whistle.
TOOT TOOT TOOT TOOT TOOT TOOT
The cow jumps away just in time.

Now Number 312 has almost reached the city.
The engineer blows a long blast to let everyone know
the train is coming.
TOOOOOOT

The engineer must not forget to warn the people
and automobiles at the many crossings.
He blows the whistle.
TOOOOT TOOOOT TOOT TOOOOT
He makes it sound like *toot toot t' toot.*
"Stop, Look, and Listen," the engineer whistles.

Now Engine Number 312 is on Track 2 in the big city railroad yard. It has pulled refrigerator cars with lettuce and bananas and meat and eggs . . . box cars with television sets and furniture and paint and toys and many other things . . . gondolas with coal . . . tank cars with oil.

Soon the freight cars will be unloaded. The bananas and the television sets and the other things will be taken to stores that are waiting for them.

But Number 312's work is done before the freight cars are unloaded.

The head brakeman uncouples the engine from the freight cars.

The engineer takes Number 312 to the roundhouse to get ready for another run.

TOOT TOOT TOOT TOOT

—*David Robert Burleigh*

What Do You Think?

1. How do trains compare with other kinds of travel like automobiles, boats, and airplanes? Explain why you like one of these best.

2. Which of the people who work on trains would you want to be? Why?

3. Many years ago, travel by train was very popular. Why do you think train travel is becoming popular again?

Taking A Closer Look

1. How do train engines talk?

2. Who receives the messages the engineer sends?

3. How do the workers get the train ready for a trip?

4. Tell how train signals are like traffic lights.

5. How do the conductor and the engineer know the train is ready to go?

6. What kinds of cars does a train engine pull? What do these cars carry?

7. Using the language of the engine, how would you signal you are ready to begin on a new activity?

Long-Ago Yesterdays

You've heard many, many stories that began "Once upon a time. . . ." Most of them were probably "make-believe" stories. Now you will go back again to "once upon a time," but the stories will be about people who lived a long time ago. In those long-ago yesterdays, many people worked hard getting America ready for *you*—today.

When someone shares a very important secret with you, it is a sign the person trusts you. Hah-nee was a young boy, not much older than you are. The secret his grandfather shared with him would change the lives of a whole family, including their dog and their crow.

Hah-nee's Secret

Long years ago, a Stone Age people lived happily in the Southwest. They hunted and planted crops and made their homes in the mountain cliffs. About six hundred years ago, the happy life of the cliff dwellers slowly changed. Rains and snow fell less and less often. Food became scarce and life was hard. The cliff dwellers were frightened.

Hah-nee, an eleven-year-old boy, lived at that time. His father and mother had no children of their own. His father found Hah-nee when he was a baby, abandoned by a neighboring, enemy people. He brought him home to Nuva, and they loved him as their own son.

The oldest, most respected member of the clan was Wupa, Hah-nee's grandfather. Wupa lived alone with his pet raven Kisha. As the story opens Kisha has taken Wupa's bag of treasured possessions and hidden it. Wupa is too old to search for it, so he has asked Hah-nee to find it for him.

Hah-nee has a friend named Tayu and a dog, Mozo. But Wupa is the person Hah-nee loves most of all. After several attempts, Hah-nee finally finds Wupa's precious bag. As the story begins, Hah-nee is on his way to give it to his grandfather.

In his excitement Hah-nee forgot he was tired and hungry. He hastened down to Wupa's[1] home, the bag in his hands. The old man was asleep on his bearskin rug as usual. Hah-nee tiptoed over to him calling, "Grandfather, wake up."

But Wupa slept on.

"Wupa, Wupa," cried Hah-nee in his ear. Wupa opened his eyes, muttering, "Oh, it's Hah-nee. What have you there? Mush for Wupa?"

"Something better than mush, Grandfather. Look."

When Wupa saw the bag he smiled happily, asking, "Where did you find this, Hah-nee?"

[1] Wupa (woo-pə)

"I was walking over the mesa and saw Kisha[1] circling in the sky over a tall pine tree. I whistled, but he would not come. He was after a squirrel I think. Then I saw something hanging on a little tree that grew right out of the face of the steep cliff. I found a stick and after trying a long time caught the bag on the stick and brought it up. Kisha must have carried it away to bury it somewhere, and it must have caught in the tree as he was flying upward."

"The old rascal," said Wupa. "Now I will hide the bag where he will never find it again. Do you know why I treasure the bag so much, Hah-nee?"

"Because you wove it when you were young?" answered Hah-nee.

"Yes, that, but something more. I have sacred things in this bag," replied Wupa, untying the red string.

"Sacred pollen?" asked Hah-nee.

[1] Kisha (KEE-shə)

"Of course, sacred pollen, and some other things. I will show you," said the old man. "Here is the sacred pollen in this bit of skin. Here are two red feathers from a parrot I got years and years ago when I went far to the south to get cotton for my wedding blanket."

"Oh," sighed Hah-nee, "they are beautiful." He fingered the bright red feathers.

"Here is the lightning knife. It is at the head of the lightning when it strikes a tree in a storm. It is very strong."

Hah-nee fingered the shining black stone shaped like an arrow point.

"But most of all, Hah-nee," said Wupa, "this white crystal here is the most valuable thing I have. The other things I could find again, but not this white crystal."

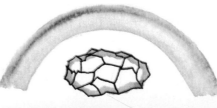

Hah-nee took the crystal, and as he turned it he saw how beautifully the light caught each side. "Where did you find this, Grandfather? It is like a rainbow after the storm."

"That is a crystal which I got years ago, the same time I got the parrot feathers and the two tiny shells in the bag. It was given to me by an old dear friend, Mai,[1] who lives far to the southeast of here, many days journey. I was very young then and so was Mai. We became great friends. He had a little son only a few years old. One day the boy was playing near his father's cornfield, and he fell asleep in a little ditch. Suddenly a cloudburst sent a wall of water down the little canyon. It happened I was close by and I dragged the boy out of the muddy water just in time. Mai never forgot. Before I left, Mai took this crystal from his bag and gave it to me saying, "Wupa if you ever need help, or any of your clan need help, this crystal in their hands will be a symbol for me to help them.' "

Hah-nee fingered the white crystal, enjoying its rare beauty. "So you know the land to the southeast, Grandfather."

"I did know it, but that was many years ago when I made that journey. It was a fair land then. A great river passed near the pueblo where Mai and his people live.

[1] Mai (MAH-ee)

They grow corn, but they never had the great dryness that we have had over the years. This is what I have been thinking, Hah-nee. The time will come one day, and soon, when you will see me as you saw me this morning. Asleep. But, Hah-nee, then you cannot awaken me, no matter how hard you try. I shall have gone on the long, long sleep, the sleep we all must make. But you must not be sad, for it is a good land to which I go."

Hah-nee felt very sad, for to lose Wupa would be like losing Mother Nuva.[1] "When will that be, Grandfather?" he asked wonderingly.

"No one knows, Hah-nee. But the long sleep is near. I feel more and more as the days go by that it is near. So, before I go, Hah-nee, I have been thinking of you and your family. I have a plan."

"A plan?" asked Hah-nee.

"Hah-nee," continued the old man, "go to the corner of the room and pull out that piece of white buckskin you see there."

Hah-nee did as the old man said. He handed the buckskin to him. Wupa unrolled it and laid it flat on the floor of the terrace. Then he said, "Now, Hah-nee, go to your room and bring back some beeweed your mother has there to paint her jars with. And a yucca-leaf brush."

[1] Nuva (NOO-və)

When Hah-nee reached his home, no one was there. On a ledge was a jar Mother Nuva had been working on. It was partly decorated. Black designs on a white ground and very beautiful.

Hah-nee found a yucca-leaf brush and a bowl of black beeweed paint. He returned to Wupa's ledge. "Here is the paint and the brush," he said. "Now what are you going to do?"

Wupa did not reply. He moistened the brush and Hah-nee watched the old man's hand tremble as he placed the brush on the buckskin.

"Watch, Hah-nee. I will draw the trail I took to the home of my friend Mai. Here is our cliff dwelling. You travel along the canyon until you come to a river. Here. It may be dry now. You cross that river and then you will see high mountains. Go to the west of them. Here, right here," and he marked a dot, "you will see a spring. Beside the spring is a very old and very green tree. Then you walk for two more suns along this trail. Then you will see a huge mountain that goes up into the sky and has a sharp point like an arrow tip. Here is another spring."

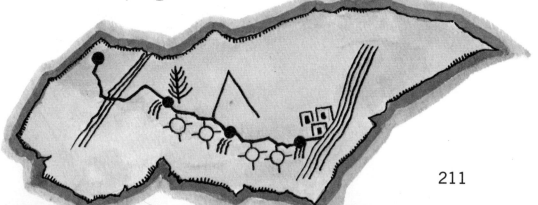

Wupa's trembling hand made another dot on the buckskin. He drew and talked at the same time. "Two more suns journey to the southeast, and here is another spring. It may not be there now, for it is many years since I went that way. Here you will finally come to a land with stone houses by a broad flowing river. It is in a straight line as a bird flies from this place." He pointed to the last spring he had drawn on the buckskin. "In that land lives my friend Mai. He is beloved of his people. I am sure by now he is a great leader among them."

"But, Grandfather," asked Hah-nee, "why do you ask us to leave our home in the cliffs?"

"I do not know if you will leave, Hah-nee. Perhaps, perhaps not. If the crops should fail and fail and fail and no rain fall, it may be you will *want* to leave the cliffs. When I go on the long sleep, people may turn against you and your family, because you are of enemy blood. Then it may be you will want to go to the land of Mai. You know, son, when people become frightened, they do many strange things. They always try to find someone to blame for their troubles. They might think that you are causing the drought, who knows? The people of the Coyote Clan, who are jealous of our fields, may remind the priests. The priests are frantic now."

"But it *may* rain," said Hah-nee hopefully.

"Yes it *may* rain and the crops *may* be good. Then the people will forget. But if the rains do not fall, people will not forget. And because I am an old, old man and have seen many people act in many ways, I made this plan for you."

The old fear gripped Hah-nee's heart and he cried out, "I do not want to leave these cliffs, Grandfather, and I do not want to leave you and Kisha."

"I know, Hah-nee. It is hard to leave the place where one has always lived, and to go far away to a place one does not know. But remember you have a friend in the far land who will help you. Think of the corn Father and Uncle Osa[1] will raise. Think of the beautiful jars Mother will make, jars out of her heart and her mind. And you will make new friends, Hah-nee, and can play the hoop game and go rabbit hunting with them. And you will never go to bed hungry."

[1] Osa (OH-sə)

Then Han-nee remembered Honani,[1] she of the child's mind, and the others who were driven from the cliffs into the desert by the maddened people. They were witches. This same thing could happen to him. The priests might need to find some new evil spirit, for the drought was long. He rolled up the buck-skin as Wupa said:

"Keep this skin and do not show it to anyone. Not until I have gone on the long, long sleep. Here is the crystal. Guard it well. Do not let Kisha see it. He would try to steal it again. He loves shiny things."

Hastily Hah-nee put the crystal in his bag. He rolled up the buckskin, for just at that moment Kisha swept into the cliff dwelling like a black arrow. He laid a dead squirrel before his master.

"You speak of that bird and here he is," said Wupa smiling. "Now go, my son, and eat. Do not tell any of the plan until the time is ready. Keep this secret locked in your heart. If the time comes when you must go on the long desert trail to the Land of Mai, think of Wupa. For he will be with you."

"What shall we do with Kisha?" asked Hah-nee.

"Kisha? Take him with you. Few people love him here, and many fear him. When I am gone they might harm him. He loves me best of all, but he will love you when I am gone. He will help you on

[1] Honani (HOH-nah-nee)

214

the way in finding game. He is a good hunter. For several days tie him to you, for he will want to return to find me. Then the people might think him evil and kill him. Take him with you," he continued, stroking Kisha's long black feathers as Kisha muttered his usual "Caw, caw," as if to say, "Yes, yes."

"Grandfather, I go now and take back the brush, the paint, and hide the buckskin," said Hah-nee, tears in his eyes.

"Go, Hah-nee, and do not be sad. Wupa goes to a good land. He does not fear. He has tried to live as his fathers have taught him. He goes to a land where his bones will be young again, and where his eyes can see far away. Where he can again hunt the deer, and hoe the corn."

Hah-nee climbed down to his home, hiding the buckskin under his sleeping mat. He sat on a rock by the fire, eating cold corn cakes and admiring Mother's beautiful jar. She will be unhappy that she cannot take it with her, he thought, but thinking of the jar made him think again of the Land of Mai. She will make many beautiful jars there, he thought. And the longer he dreamed of the journey the happier he became. The fear of the people's wrath as the drought continued had begun to burden him. So within the boy's heart came the hope of knowing new places and new people, and he grew happier as he thought of the land he would soon see.

—*Mary and Conrad Buff*

What Do You Think?

1. Why do you suppose Hah-nee liked to spend so much time with Wupa?
2. How do you think Wupa felt having his grandson spend so much time with him?
3. Why did Wupa feel the people might turn against Hah-nee?

Taking a Closer Look

1. Why did Wupa treasure his bag so much?
2. Explain why the crystal meant more to him than anything else in the bag.
3. Why was it important to Wupa to give Hah-nee the crystal?
4. How was Hah-nee to find the land of Mai?
5. When was he to go to Mai?
6. What plan did Wupa make for Kisha?
7. What was Hah-nee's secret?
8. When would he be free to share it?
9. Why hadn't the people turned against Hah-nee before this?

How will Hah-nee know when to tell his grandfather's secret? As you meet Hah-nee's friend Tayu[1] and see what happens to Mother Nuva's jar and the family's garden, *you* will know when Hah-nee should tell *both* his secrets.

[1] Tayu (TIGH-YOO)

The Land of Mai

It was hard for Hah-nee to keep Wupa's secret to himself. Often he would creep into his hut when everyone was away and study the picture Wupa had painted on the buckskin. He saw the river they must cross; the cottonwood tree at the spring; the mountain with a point like an arrow. But most of all the land of the Great River. Often he took out the white crystal from his bag and enjoyed its beautiful colors. He thought of the day he would show it to Mai. And the more he dreamed of the new land the more eager he was to go away. As the hot days dragged on, he felt that the people were more and more unfriendly. Or did he only *think* so? The boys threw rocks in his direction when he passed by their home, and called out names after him.

August ended and the rains did not come. September was just as hot. All night in the kivas[1] the priests prayed, fasted, chanted, and used every charm they knew to try to please the gods. Nothing that they did brought the longed-for rain. The sun rose each morning hot in a cloudless sky. Much of the small game disappeared, rabbits, squirrels, mice, birds. It was hard to find even a little field mouse. People were really hungry, but more than that they feared their gods had deserted them.

[1] kivas (KEE-vəz)

Early one morning as Hah-nee was returning from his all-night field duty, he climbed to Wupa's cell. Wupa lay on his bearskin rug as usual, sound asleep. Hah-nee had seen him that way for many years. But this time when he tried to awaken him, he could not. The old man had gone on the long, long sleep he had so often wished for. Hah-nee was frightened. He called for his mother. Everyone was unhappy. Everyone was sad. But Wupa looked so peaceful lying on his bearskin that it was hard for Hah-nee to weep as did the others. He remembered what Wupa had told him, that he would be young again in the land to which he was going.

They wrapped Wupa in a cotton and feather blanket, and buried him in a shallow grave at the rear of his cell. They placed food, water, his precious bag, his bow and arrow, his tools beside him. He might need them in the world to come.

Each morning, for three days, Mother Nuva placed water and food on Wupa's grave. On the morning of the fourth day his spirit would leave his body and enter the earth through the spirit hole in the kiva.

On the morning of the third day after Wupa's death, Mother Nuva and Father and Uncle Osa became frightened. Something terrible had happened during the night. When Father went to look at his withering corn, he found two rows completely stripped of ears. All the squash was gone too. Then, when he came to tell his wife, he found her in tears. During the night someone had thrown a rock at her beautiful new jar, and it lay on the terrace in many small pieces. Everything was happening at once.

That night the family sat around their fire, thinking sadly of their cornfield and the broken jar, and Wupa's death. They were wondering if there would be enough corn for the winter ahead. Suddenly Hah-nee heard his friend Tayu whistle. He slipped from the fire to the edge of the cliff.

"Hah-nee," whispered Tayu, "come. I have something to tell you."

The two boys found an abandoned storehouse and sat down in the darkness.

"Hah-nee," said Tayu, "I am your friend. I have always been your friend. We have played together and worked together always. But now I can be your friend no longer."

"Why is that, Tayu?" whispered Hah-nee. "What has happened?"

"My father forbids me to see you. He says the people say you are an enemy. They whisper that you are working with evil spirits. Some even say you are the one who has caused the long drought. Siki,[1] that old gossip of the Coyote Clan, says the drought started when you first came here. If you go away it will rain, she says."

"She says that?" exclaimed Hah-nee. "How did you learn of this?"

"My brother, who is in the kiva now, for he is to be a priest, told me. Tomorrow it will be four days since Wupa died. His spirit enters the spirit hole in the kiva at dawn. Then, Hah-nee, if you are still here, I fear for you. You may be dragged before the council of the elders and no one knows what the council might do with you."

"Will they harm the rest of my family, do you think?"

"I do not know. But when people are afraid, as they are now, it is hard to say what they will do. You remember how they chased old Honani away?"

[1] Siki (SEE-kee)

"Yes," answered Hah-nee, his heart beating fast with fear.

"I must go now, for they might miss me. My father would be very angry if he knew I warned you."

The boy slipped quietly away in the darkness. Hah-nee sat in the storeroom for a while thinking what he should do. He was very much afraid. Perhaps this was the time to tell his family of Wupa's plan. He slipped back to the fire and sat beside his mother.

"Was that Tayu?" she asked.

"Yes," replied Hah-nee. "It was Tayu." He darted quickly into his room and returned with the buckskin in his hand. He laid it out on the stone terrace before the fire, saying, "Now the time has come that I must tell you a secret I have known for a long, long time — Wupa's secret and mine."

The three before the fire looked at the boy in wonder. He took up a stick, and as he traced the black line on the buckskin, he said, "Tayu says the people are afraid of me. Someone broke Mother's jar. Someone else stole the corn and squash. It is now as Wupa warned. He said that harm might come to us as soon as his spirit enters the new world."

"But what are you doing with that stick, Hah-nee? What is that line you are drawing on the buckskin?" asked Father.

"That is the trail we should take to the new land of Mai, Father. Wupa drew this trail on the buckskin with beeweed before he died. He has a very old friend in a land far to the southeast by the Great River. His name is Mai." Hah-nee pointed with the stick to the bottom of the buckskin. "It is many days journey to the Land of Mai. Wupa was there when he was young. He gave me this white crystal, and said that Mai had given it to him for saving the life of his little son. Mai told Wupa years ago that he would be kind to any who brought him the crystal."

Then Hah-nee explained the trail. He pointed to the river, the springs, the mountain with a point like an arrow, and the mesa by the Great River.

"And you have kept this secret for a long time, Hah-nee?" asked Father with wondering eyes.

"Yes, for a long time, Father," said Hah-nee proudly. "Wupa warned me not to say a word, for if I did the priests might learn of it. At dawn tomorrow Wupa's spirit enters the new world. After that Wupa will not be here to protect us."

"So it is," said Father.

"So it is," said Uncle Osa. "Then we must go tonight. Tonight when all are sleeping."

"I suppose we must," said Mother sadly, "although I do not wish to go."

With no more words the family prepared for the long

224

journey. They gathered what little seed corn they had, and some dried corn meal. Uncle Osa filled two canteens with water. Hah-nee put a pile of *piñon*[1] nuts in his carrying bag. He tied Kisha to his shoulder. Kisha was sleepy and cross.

At midnight, when a new moon was still in the sky, the four, followed by their dog Mozo,[2] crept silently down the ladders and toe holds into the canyon for the last time. They took the well-worn path down the canyon. As it turned, Mother Nuva and Hah-nee looked back at the Great City they had known always, now dark and silent in deep shadow. A fire flickered here and there against a stone wall; a turkey gobbled. The ancient cliffs. Their old home. The home they would never see again. Then they hurried after the men.

Mozo, as the trail passed under some smaller cliff dwellings, growled; so Hah-nee tied his mouth with a strong yucca fiber. They feared someone might see them slipping quietly away. Once they passed a late hunter on the trail, but they did not know him nor did he know them.

[1] *piñon* (PEE-nyohn)   [2] Mozo (MOH-zoh)

They came to the river at dawn. Not one drop of water flowed over the sand. All that day Hah-nee's family plodded on through the heat and dust. Often they unrolled the map that Wupa had drawn on the buckskin and studied it carefully. A day later they came to the land of the high mountains and found the spring. But the old tree was gone.

Two more suns and they reached the mountain with the sharp peak like an arrow but found no spring. That night, as they camped, Uncle Osa and Father dug a deep hole in the sand. In the morning, as Hah-nee looked into the hole he saw water had seeped up from below. They all drank deeply of the cool water. Filling their clay jars, they stumbled on, ever southeast.

On the morning of the sixth day, a desert sandstorm suddenly blotted out sky, mountains, and trail. As the hot sands swirled about them, the family found refuge between great rocks. All day long they lay there trying to breathe through the wet rags over their faces. Kisha tucked his head under his wing and slept.

As Hah-nee lay close to his mother, he whispered, "Mother, do you think we will EVER, EVER, get to the land of Mai? My throat and eyes hurt so."

Nuva answered wearily, "I don't know, my son, we can only hope and try to keep on the trail that Wupa drew for us."

The next day they hurried along, Hah-nee, Uncle Osa, Mother Nuva, and Father, each thinking his own thoughts. Mother was thinking of beautiful jars she would make in the land to come. Father and Uncle Osa saw rows and rows of tall green corn with golden tassels, fat squash, and jars full of brown shining beans in the land of the Great River.

In the morning the air was clear and they could see for miles in every direction. Hah-nee untied the string around Kisha's leg and let him fly away to hunt for food. Many hours later he returned, a lean jack rabbit dangling from his bill. Suddenly everybody felt better. They knew they would have something to eat. After supper, by the light of the fire, the men made new moccasins. Their old ones were torn to shreds by sand, rocks, and the sharp spines of cactus everywhere over the desert.

As the days went by, the desert began to grow more green. They came to a beautiful cottonwood tree and rested in its shade. It was wonderful to see a green tree again. Then they walked on and on until it was quite dark. Camping in a deep sandy gully, they were so tired that they slept all through the night.

Before dawn, Hah-nee was awakened by the sound of rustling leaves. Was he dreaming of the cornfields of home? Then he heard the faint sound of an Indian flute. He climbed hastily up the sandy ravine. As he stood in the dim light of dawn he could not believe what he saw. Before him was a vast field of corn, the green leaves rustling in the wind. Beyond the cornfield rose a great rocky mesa.

They had reached the Land of Mai.

And Hah-nee, as he held tight to Kisha's leash, thought often of Wupa, whose spirit and faith he felt with him. He thought of the friends he was leaving, especially Tayu; of the sweet sound of the flute player welcoming the sun. He was wondering who would play with him in the land of Mai. Would Mai have a grandson? What would Mai look like? But most of all for Hah-nee, the sorrows and fears of the past month began to fade away. He would make new friends. No one here would call him FUNNYHEAD or UTE.[1] He would be the son of Nuva, come from the far-off land of the Northwest, the land of the Cliff Dwellers.

[1] Ute (YOOT)

Thus
Went Hah-nee and his family
Into the wilderness
As others had gone
Before them

Days of wandering
Days of hunger and thirst
Days of danger
Lay before Hah-nee and his family
Until they reached the distant land
The land of Mai.
The land of a flowing river
The Great Rio Grande

There
Upon a broad mesa
They found friends
They built a new home
The land grew high with corn
And they were content

So it was with many other
Dwellers of the cliffs
As the years of drought dragged on
Twenty-four long years.

The cliff cities of the canyons
Of the Great Southwest
Slowly fell to ruin

Only the owl hooted there
As the rat scurried in and out
And the wind whined about empty homes
For the people had gone
To mingle with other peoples far to the south
Leaving their ancient homes
Forever

And today
As one stumbles through the dust
Of silent rooms
And peers into the empty kivas
Where once priests prayed for rain
One lives again
That ancient life
Forgotten for six hundred years
The life of Hah-nee
Of the Cliff Country

—Mary and Conrad Buff

What Do You Think?

1. When Wupa died, why was Hah-nee the only one who did not cry?

2. How do you suppose Hah-nee's family felt when they realized the tribe was turning against them?

3. Why was it so hard for Hah-nee's family to leave their home?

4. What things would Hah-nee wonder about as he came to Mai?

Taking A Closer Look

1. What did the family do to prepare Wupa for his journey to the spirit world?

2. Before Tayu told Hah-nee, how did the family know that the tribe was turning against them?

3. Why did Tayu tell Hah-nee?

4. Explain why the family left at night.

5. What did they take with them?

6. Tell about some of the problems the family faced as they traveled.

7. Why was Hah-nee happy to get to Mai?

Ships are for sailing. Youth is the time to dream long dreams. When ships and a dreamer get together, you can expect surprises. Before he ever knew he would discover America, Columbus dreamed and sailed. Does this make *your* dreams seem more important?

232

THIS DREAM CAME TRUE

Characters

CHRISTOPHER COLUMBUS

DOMENICO,[1] his father

SIGNORA[2] **COLUMBUS,** his mother

PEDRO,[3] his friend

Costumes

CHRISTOPHER COLUMBUS, *the boy, wears a knee-length tunic with flowing sleeves. It is belted at the waist and attached to the belt is a leather coin purse.*

PEDRO *is dressed similarly to* **COLUMBUS** *the boy.*

DOMINICO *wears a long, loose gown of rich-looking material. It is belted at the waist with a scarf. From his shoulders hangs an ankle-length cape.*

SIGNORA COLUMBUS *wears a long, loose simple gown.*

Properties

Scene One: simple furnishings *of a weaving room, including several chairs and a loom with cloth stretched over it, also a scroll.*

Scene Two: kitchen furnishings, table and chairs, a letter.

Scene Three: kitchen furnishings, table, chairs, a packet.

[1] Domenico (doh-MAY-nee-koh) [2] Signora (seen-YOR-ə)
[3] Pedro (PAY-droh)

233

Scene One

TIME: *The year 1465.*

PLACE: *The weaving room of* DOMENICO COLUMBUS *in Genoa,[1] Italy. When the curtain rises, fourteen-year-old* CHRISTOPHER *is seen seated before the loom, but his hands are idle. He is reading from a scroll.*

(DOMENICO *enters the room.*)

DOMENICO: Cristoforo!

CHRISTOPHER: Yes, Father?

DOMENICO: You are reading again, though I told you to keep at your weaving. Have I not told you that this cloth must be ready before this week is passed?

CHRISTOPHER: Yes, Father. But . . . *(He hangs his head for a moment, then looks his father straight in the eye.)* I am tired of weaving! I do not like to weave. But this tale, Father—it is wonderful! *(He rises, holding the scroll in his hands.)* This is what I like, what I want to be. Yes, I want to be like Marco Polo. You should read

[1] *Genoa* (JEN-oh-ə)

it, Father—all about the wonderful travels he had, the strange sights he saw. *He* was afraid of nothing. Oh, if only I could be a sailor!

DOMENICO: What is this nonsense? Always the same, always this talk of becoming a sailor!

CHRISTOPHER: When I am grown I *shall* be a sailor. Not only that, but a great one, too.

DOMENICO: You shall be nothing of the kind! My son shall be a weaver like his father. And you must keep at your work, Cristoforo, and stop this talk of sailing and navigating, I tell you. How can a boy of fourteen know what he wants to be when he is older?

CHRISTOPHER: I *know* what I want! When I am a man I shall follow in the footsteps of Marco Polo and travel over all the world. I shall have ships that sail the seas, and I shall be their master!

DOMENICO: Let me hear no further talk of this kind. Now give me that scroll and get back to your weaving at once! *(He takes the scroll from* **CHRISTOPHER'S** *hands.)*

*(*DOMENICO *leaves and* PEDRO *enters.)*

PEDRO: What, Cristoforo! You sit at the weaving while a new ship has come into port—a strange and wonderful ship—and you not there to see her! All of Genoa was there to watch her dock. What a beautiful sight that was as she entered the harbor with her sails flying!

CHRISTOPHER: How could I be there when my father keeps me at the loom? Do not bother me, Pedro. This cloth must be finished and sold. My family can use the money it will bring.

PEDRO: Well, there is still time for you to see her at the wharves. She will be in dock for three days, then set forth once more.

CHRISTOPHER: Pedro, I wish I might sail with her. With all my heart, I do.

PEDRO: What, *you* a sailor? *(He laughs.)* That's funny. You are little more than a boy. *(He tilts his head to one side and studies* CHRISTOPHER.*)* Though I must say you are grown tall for your age, Cristoforo.

CHRISTOPHER: I am just fourteen, but I know as much about ships and sailing and charts and maps as many a grown-up!

PEDRO: *(Taking a letter from his pocket)* Here, I almost forgot my real reason for coming. I have a letter for your father. Strangely enough, Cristoforo, this letter was handed me by a sailor from the same ship I have been telling you about. Your father must be an important person to receive letters from foreign shores.

CHRISTOPHER: My father is not only a weaver, he is also a merchant of fine cloth and receives orders from many places. *(He goes to right of stage and calls to his father.)* Father, where are you? Come quickly — Pedro has brought an order for you.

(DOMENICO *enters.*)

DOMENICO: What is this?

PEDRO: A letter for you, *signor. (He hands the letter to* DOMENICO, DOMENICO *reads it.)*

DOMENICO: This is unfortunate.

CHRISTOPHER: Is something wrong, Father?

DOMENICO: *Si, si.* The very cloth you are working on, my son. Yes, most unfortunate, this. *(He sits at the table and puts his head in his hands.* CHRISTOPHER *moves closer to him.)*

CHRISTOPHER: Does the gentleman not want it after all?

DOMENICO: Well, yes. He wants it. But he was to have come to Genoa for it. Now he cannot come. He wants me to send it to him, all the way to Corsica.[1]

PEDRO: Perhaps you could send it to him by the same sailor who carried the letter, *signor.*

DOMENICO: No, no! I do not know these sailors. This cloth is worth much money. Would the sailor bring back all of it, think you? I do not trust them.

[1] Corsica (KOR-si-kə)

CHRISTOPHER: Father. Father . . .

DOMENICO: Yes, yes, boy, speak up!

CHRISTOPHER: Father, let me take the cloth to the man!

PEDRO: *(Laughing)* You, Cristoforo? Ha, ha, that is funny!

DOMENICO: Is it so funny? *(He looks at* CHRISTOPHER *for a moment without speaking. Then he rises and goes to* CHRISTOPHER, *placing his hands on his son's shoulders.)* My son, you have grown tall these past weeks.

CHRISTOPHER: Yes, Father. And I am strong. And I can take care of myself.

DOMENICO: I believe you could. Yes, Cristoforo, I believe you could make this journey. I shall try to sign you on as deck hand on the ship that rests in the harbor.

CHRISTOPHER: Then I may go? Pedro, do you hear? I shall sail on that very ship which you have just been begging me to see. It seems too good to be true.

DOMENICO: I shall go at once to see the ship's captain.

CHRISTOPHER: And I shall go with you.

DOMENICO: No. You are forgetting, Son, that there is still much work to be done on the cloth. You will stay here and work.

CHRISTOPHER: Oh yes, Father. *(He runs to the loom and seats himself before it.)* I shall waste no time, never fear!

Curtain

Scene Two

TIME: *Several weeks later.*

PLACE: *The kitchen of the* COLUMBUS *home.* DOMENICO *and* SIGNORA COLUMBUS *are seated at the table.*

SIGNORA COLUMBUS: It still seems strange in this house without our son Cristoforo. The other children miss him.

DOMENICO: And you, Mother, you miss him too.

SIGNORA COLUMBUS: *(Sighing deeply)* It is not just that I miss him, my husband. There is fear in my heart.

DOMENICO: He will come back safely, and he will bring the money which we need to feed our children. Cristoforo is always to be relied upon.

SIGNORA COLUMBUS: My fears are for the future. I know the lad better than anyone, for I am his mother. I know what is in his heart. The sea is in his heart, Domenico! He talks of little else. He learns quickly, and when he returns from this, his first voyage, he will have learned much about the sea. But Cristoforo will want to know more!

DOMENICO: You are trying to say that from now on he will follow the sea, are you not?

SIGNORA COLUMBUS: Yes, our son will follow the sea.

DOMENICO: You are probably right, Mother. He has told me the same, and always I have discouraged him. Well, if it is in his heart and soul, as you say, I shall complain no more. And now I must go into the weaving room to see how the new boy is making out. He is young yet and *(He laughs.)* he is not Cristoforo!

(**DOMENICO** *goes out.*)

Curtain

Scene Three

TIME: *The following day.*

PLACE: *The kitchen of the* **COLUMBUS** *home.* **SIGNORA COLUMBUS** *is seated at the table with her head on her arms.*

(**DOMENICO** *enters after a moment.*)

DOMENICO: Do you sleep, my wife? *(She raises her head and looks at him.)*

SIGNORA COLUMBUS: Domenico! I have just had the strangest dream.

DOMENICO: Ah, but you always have strange dreams!

SIGNORA COLUMBUS: But this was about our son Cristoforo.

DOMENICO: It is about Cristoforo that I have come to speak to you. We shall see him any moment. His ship is in the harbor!

SIGNORA COLUMBUS: But the dream was so real, Domenico! I must tell Cristoforo about it.

DOMENICO: Well, you may tell him now, for here is our son!

(Enter CHRISTOPHER *from side.)*

CHRISTOPHER: You are right, Father. I am back, safe and sound. And here is the money for the cloth. *(He hands a packet to* DOMENICO, *then turns toward his mother.)* And what is it you would tell me, Mother?

SIGNORA COLUMBUS: *(Kissing her son on his forehead)* I am so filled with joy that you have returned, my son, that it has almost wiped the dream from my mind. Tell me, Cristoforo, have you brought back treasures from your voyage?

CHRISTOPHER: *(Laughing)* No treasure, Mother. Just Father's payment for the cloth that I was able to deliver. Oh, yes, and something else too.

DOMENICO AND SIGNORA: *(Together)* What is that?

CHRISTOPHER: An agreement with the captain to continue on his ship! And this next time we are to make an even longer voyage.

SIGNORA COLUMBUS: *(Looking at her husband)* A longer voyage! You see, Domenico, he must follow the sea. Yes, he must follow the sea, for it is his destiny. Can you understand that, my husband? It will be as in my dream!

CHRISTOPHER: What is this dream?

SIGNORA COLUMBUS: While I slept just now, I had a strange dream of you, Cristoforo. In that dream I seemed to see you as you will be years from now, perhaps long after I have left this world. It was so real I cannot help but think that it was meant to show me what the future holds in store for you, my son!

CHRISTOPHER: Was I a sailor, Mother?

SIGNORA COLUMBUS: Oh, more than a sailor! The queen called you "Admiral of the Ocean Seas." You kissed her hand and spoke to both the king and queen as though they were your equals. You spoke of foreign shores you had discovered, and great treasure. You asked for more ships to be put under your command, and they were promised you! You were a *very* great man in my dream, my son.

DOMENICO: Listen to her! She talks as though she believes all this nonsense of kings and queens and treasures. But it is very natural, I suppose.

SIGNORA COLUMBUS: But Father, the queen called Cristoforo a hero, and said that his name would become famous over all the world!

DOMENICO: *(Laughing)* Well, now that you have had a good sleep, wife, let us have some supper. I am sure that Cristoforo is very hungry.

(They start to leave the room. **DOMENICO** *goes off stage at right. When* **CHRISTOPHER** *and his mother approach the door, however, she stops him and takes his hand in hers.)*

SIGNORA COLUMBUS: Cristoforo, I have something to say to you.

CHRISTOPHER: Yes, Mother?

SIGNORA COLUMBUS: *(In a serious voice)* This was no ordinary dream I had, nor half-waking fancy! It was

too real for that. I am sure it was meant to reveal to me, your mother, the truth of what the future holds in store for you. Yes, my son, I believe with all my heart that this dream will one day come true! It is your destiny, Cristoforo Columbus, to become world famous. *(She places her hand over her heart.)* I feel it here, in my heart!

CHRISTOPHER: *(Dreamily and gazing off into space)* Perhaps you are right, my mother. Who knows?

Curtain

—Elizabeth H. Sechrist

244

What Do You Think?

1. What did Christopher's father think of him?

2. Why was Christopher interested in the sea?

3. If Christopher were alive today, what would he probably be interested in exploring?

4. Christopher lived about 500 years ago. Even so, why does he seem like some of your friends?

Taking A Closer Look

1. What did Christopher like to do better than to weave?

2. How did Christopher get his first chance to go on a voyage?

3. Why did Christopher's father want him to become a weaver and a merchant?

4. What did Christopher's father think about Christopher going to sea in the future?

5. Did Christopher's mother feel the same way? Why?

6. How do you know how much she thought about Christopher and his dream of the sea?

Rat-a-tat-tat! Rum-dee-dee-dum-dum-dum! Even the drums were excited on the first Thanksgiving Day. Meet the people who were there on that day. Play with baby Oceanus, born on the *Mayflower,* and with his brother Giles and sister Damaris. Smell the roast turkey and duck, and clam stew. Watch the dance and listen to the prayers of thanks. Look back to a long-ago yesterday—back more than three hundred years.

Pilgrim Thanksgiving

Damaris Hopkins opened her eyes and sat up in bed, listening. Suddenly she remembered. This was the day Governor Bradford had invited the Indians to come to a feast of thanksgiving.

"Our corn and other crops are gathered in," he had said. "We must give thanks. We have been able to grow enough food to feed us in the long winter ahead. And we must invite our neighbors, the Indians, to our thanksgiving feast. They gave us the seed of the corn to plant. And our Indian friend, Squanto,[1] taught us how to plant it. Yes, they must be invited."

Governor Bradford had sent four men into the woods to hunt wild turkeys and ducks and deer for the feast. The holiday was to last three days.

Damaris heard her older brother, Giles, turn in his straw bed nearby. He sat up, rubbing his eyes. Remembering the holiday, Giles jumped out of bed and pulled on breeches and jacket over the long underwear he had worn all night to help keep him warm. Then he went down the ladder of split logs nailed against the wall into the one room of the house.

[1] Squanto (SKWAHN-toh)

Damaris heard her mother say, "Good morning, Giles." She could smell corn-meal porridge cooking for breakfast. She got out of bed and got dressed. Then she went down the rough ladder.

Her mother was feeding porridge to little Oceanus, the baby brother who had been born on the *Mayflower*. He was a year old now. When he saw Damaris, he bounced up and down and beat on his wooden dish with his pewter spoon.

Damaris laughed. Oceanus was such a happy baby.

Mother smiled. "Maybe he feels how excited we all are," she said. "Now we must hurry. We must finish the cooking."

"That's what we've been doing for days," Damaris said.

She hurried and ate her corn porridge. Then she watched the turkey roasting on the spit in the fireplace. Every few minutes she turned the iron hook that held the turkey over the hot coals. She wanted the turkey to be roasted evenly on all sides. If she didn't turn it, it would burn. The good roasting smell made Damaris so hungry she could hardly wait for dinner.

She was glad when her mother said she could go and help the other children set the table outdoors. Not even the Common House was big enough to hold the guests for the feast. The men had built a long table of planks in the clearing away from the houses.

As Damaris carried a kettle of corn pudding out of the house, Master Goodman's little dog ran to meet her. He leaped up and barked. He licked her hand. She held the kettle higher.

"No, no, Little Dog," she said. "I know how hungry you are but you must wait, too."

Little Dog stayed close to her. He frisked about her feet so that she almost tripped over him as she carried dishes of food. But she laughed. He was such a loving, funny little dog, even if he wasn't very brave.

Little Dog was afraid of all kinds of loud noises. The other children sometimes laughed at him when he put his tail between his legs and ran. But Damaris knew what it was to be afraid. She petted the little dog. He liked to hide beneath her long full skirts. Oh yes, from there, he peeped out quite bravely.

Damaris went back and forth from the house with food. From the woods, came the sound of a trumpet, then a drum. Earlier that morning, Captain Standish and a group of Pilgrim men had gone to meet the Indians. Now, the drum sounds came nearer.

Rat-a-tat-tat! Rum-dee-dee-dum-dum-dum!

Mothers came from the houses. Children ran to stand near the table. All looked toward the woods.

Captain Standish came from the woods first. He was not so tall as the other men, but he was straight and fearless. Behind him came a few Pilgrim men with muskets. Then came the Indians.

Their chief, Massasoit,[1] led them. He was tall and walked proudly. Behind him came other Indian men. Some of them carried wild turkey and deer meat for the feast.

The Indians wore leggings and a kind of shirt made of deerskin. Their hair was very black and long. It was cut in front so that it would not hang in their eyes.

They kept coming from the woods and coming from the woods. Damaris could not count fast enough to know how many there were. But she knew there were many more Indians than Pilgrims. There were only twenty white men and six growing boys left in all the Pilgrim village. There were a few women. More than half the Pilgrims were children.

Damaris heard her brother Giles counting softly. Then he said to his friend Richard Moore, who stood beside him, "I count ninety."

[1] Massasoit (MAS-ə-SOIT)

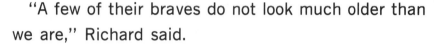

"A few of their braves do not look much older than we are," Richard said.

"Perhaps they were allowed to come because they are good at the races and dances," Giles said.

"Father says the Indians will do some of their dances after the dinner. See that young brave with the wild-cat tail around his neck. He is about my size. I will try to make friends with him."

When the welcoming was over, the women and children hurried to put the food on the long plank table. The men began to sit down on benches at the table. Chief Massasoit and Governor Bradford sat at the head. A few of the older Indian braves sat at the table with the Pilgrim men. Most of the other Indians sat on the ground.

Then the table was loaded with roast turkey and ducks. With clam stew and venison stew. With bread pudding and corn pudding. With vegetables and a sweet cake made with dried berries. The women and children sat down at the table.

Elder Brewster was ready to give thanks. Damaris lowered her head quickly. For a long time she kept her eyes almost closed. How good everything smelled. How long Elder Brewster prayed. Damaris felt her stomach groan. She was so hungry.

After Elder Brewster sat down, Governor Bradford prayed. Damaris saw how politely the Indians listened. How quiet they were although they could not understand a word. They seemed to know that this was the white man's way of saying thank you to the Great Father who takes care of all people.

After the prayers, everyone began to eat. Damaris kept putting scraps of skin and meat on the ground behind her for Little Dog. Several times she left the table to help bring more food.

After a while she saw her brother Giles stand up and go over to the young Indian with the wildcat tail around his neck. Giles smiled at the young brave and squatted down beside him.

Damaris saw the young Indian looking at the hunting knife stuck in Giles' belt. Giles was very proud of the sharp knife. His father had given it to him for his birthday. When he saw the Indian look at it, Giles took the knife from his belt and let the Indian take it. The young Indian turned it over and over. He held up a coarse hair from the wildcat tail and touched the knife to it. The hair split in two. The young brave smiled.

"Take it," Giles said. "It is a present. Take it."

The young Indian could not understand the words. He held the knife against his heart.

Giles nodded. "Yes. Take it. It is a present from me to you."

Damaris could hardly believe her ears. Giles had an old knife but this knife was his best one. He liked it better than anything else he had. Yet he had given it to the Indian boy.

Damaris saw the joy that came over the Indian boy's face. He reached down and picked up his tomahawk. He handed it to Giles. Giles took the tomahawk gravely. The Indian boy made signs that Giles was to keep it.

Damaris heard Giles say, "Thank you."

At last even the hungriest Indian and Pilgrim were full. It was time for the hymns and dances and speeches. Bonfires were lighted for warmth and for light as the early night came on. The Pilgrims and Indians drew near the fires. The Pilgrims sang hymns. The Indians chanted the songs of their people.

253

Then Captain Standish gave a parade. He marched his men up the one street past the houses and back again. The Indians sat and watched.

When Captain Standish and his men sat down, some of the Indians stood up. Dusk was coming now. Damaris thought the Indians seemed very tall in the firelight.

They made a circle. They hunched forward. They began to dance. They bent and rose. They bent to the ground again. She watched them, puzzled. What did this dance mean? They seemed to be picking something up and putting it down again.

She saw them hold out their hands. They wiggled their fingers. They stamped upon the ground. And suddenly Damaris knew. This must be the dance of the planting of the corn.

How well she remembered Squanto teaching her and all the other Pilgrims how to dig holes in the earth. They took a herring fish from the basketful they had caught in the brook. Three herring in a hill. A little soil pushed over the herring with the toe, then several

kernels of Indian corn. More soil pushed over the corn. The soil stamped down with their feet.

This was the way the Indians had always planted corn, Squanto had said. And this was the way the braves were dancing now.

Damaris saw the Indians lift their hands and look toward the forest and make loud noises. This was to frighten off the wolves.

She knew. She had done everything they were doing in the dance.

Damaris looked at the Common House. There the ripe ears of corn were drying. She had helped to pick the corn and hang it there. She was proud that she had helped to raise the corn which they would eat.

At the end of the corn dance, each Indian tossed a handful of corn upon hot stones beside the fire. The corn began to hop and jump about on the hot stones. Then—*pop, pop, pop!* Kernels of corn leaped into the air. They popped open. They were like large white snowflakes flying through the air.

Damaris caught one and put it into her mouth. She knew it was good to eat. Squanto had shown the children this kind of corn which would pop open when it was hot. Popcorn.

Another kernel fell near her. Little Dog came out from under her skirts and sniffed at it. Damaris took up the white kernel. She let Little Dog eat it from her fingers. He frisked happily at her feet.

"You like popcorn," she said. "It is a gift from the Indians."

Thoughtfully she looked at the Indians. The dancers had gone back to sit in the circle now. Their faces were all turned to look at Governor Bradford. He was standing to make a goodnight speech.

The Indians listened politely. Later, Squanto would tell them all that Governor Bradford had said. Squanto could speak English as well as the language of his own people.

"We are your friends," the governor said. "And you are our friends."

Damaris saw the Indians nod as if they understood that he liked them.

"Some other white men have not treated you well," he said to the Indians. "Some white men came to this land and stole your furs and went away.

"We will not leave. It has been hard to grow enough food to keep us alive, but we have done it. You helped us learn how. We have built homes. We trade with you. We give you knives and iron cooking pots. You pay us with furs you trap in the woods.

"Do not fear that we will leave to go back over the ocean, no matter how hard it is to live in this wild land. We are not easily discouraged.

"We love freedom. We came here to be free. We came to worship God as we believe to be right. We will stay and make this our home."

Governor Bradford sat down. There was a murmuring among the Indians. Some nodded their heads.

Then Damaris saw her father stand up. Other fathers and mothers stood. It was time to go to bed.

Damaris and Giles walked together. Little Dog trotted at their heels. When they came to Master Goodman's house, they left Little Dog.

"Rest well, Little Dog," Damaris said. "Tomorrow will be another feast day. And the day after that, too. Perhaps we shall do this every year when the crops are in."

Later, when she and Giles were in their straw beds in the loft of their home, Giles said, "What a wonderful day. Did you ever have so much fun?"

Damaris did not answer. She was thinking. It had been fun. So much good food all at one time. The friendly dances of the Indians. The pride and happiness in knowing that the Common House was full of corn that she had helped to raise. The peace and trust she now felt in her heart as she listened to Governor Bradford.

Damaris was happy.

—*Wilma Pitchford Hays*

What Do You Think?

1. Why were the Pilgrims so thankful for food?
2. Why did Governor Bradford invite the Indians to the Thanksgiving feast?
3. What does Thanksgiving mean to you? Did reading this story help you understand the meaning of Thanksgiving?
4. What made you feel that Damaris and Giles are much like you and your friends?

Taking A Closer Look

1. What did the Pilgrims serve at the Thanksgiving feast?
2. How many of Massasoit's people went to the feast?
3. What made the gifts Giles and his new Indian friend gave each other very special?
4. What did Damaris remember that Squanto had taught the Pilgrims?
5. Tell what Governor Bradford talked about in his speech after dinner.
6. Why did Damaris and Giles enjoy the day so much?

"Yankee Doodle Came to Town!"
To a town near Boston. To a
lighthouse in that town. It all
happened one day in 1812. The
tune rang out boldly from
behind a sand dune. And that's
how Beckie's fife and Abbie's
drum changed the plans of some
British soldiers — and the future
of your America!

An Army in Pigtails

Once upon a time on a rockbound New England coast, there lived two sisters. Their names were Rebecca and Abigail Bates, but they became known far and wide as Beckie the fifer, and Abbie the drummer.

They came by these musical nicknames because one day something happened that no one ever expected would happen.

Beckie and Abbie lived with their father and mother and a yellow cat named Penelope. Their home was a snowy white cottage that nestled beside a tall lighthouse. The lighthouse stood on a point that jutted into the wide blue ocean. It was right at the edge of the village of Scituate[1] and not too far from Boston.

Mr. Bates, their father, was the keeper of the lighthouse. His wife and daughters were helpers. Even the cat had a share in this important work. Penelope was the lighthouse mousekeeper.

"Mind the bright work, and be sure everything is 'shipshape and Bristol fashion,' " Mr. Bates would sing out in his best seagoing voice. "Fall to, me hearties."

[1] Scituate (SIT-you-ət)

"Aye, aye sir," Beckie and Abbie would reply, and fall to like good sailors. They would polish the big light until its beams could be seen for miles around. Many a ship was brought safely into Scituate Harbor after nightfall by following its light.

But after they helped make the lighthouse "ship-shape and Bristol fashion," the girls practiced their music lessons.

Now this was in the year eighteen hundred and twelve, and people said Mr. Bates was raising an American Army of Two. As it turned out, they were not too far from the truth.

Evenings, the girls practiced by candlelight in the big keeping room of the cottage. If the sea was calm, their father came down from caring for the light to help with their music lessons.

No matter how calm the sea was on these musical evenings, Penelope, the cat, was never calm.

Penelope would disappear through a small poke hole in the door that had been made especially so she could go in and out at will.

Whenever Mr. Bates came down the winding stone stairs of the lighthouse, Penelope went out, mewing unhappily to herself. Another evening of fifing and drumming was on the way.

Mr. Bates would place an open sheet of music on a chair. Then he would rap for attention with his baton.

"All aboard, me hearties, anchors aweigh," and the keeper of the lighthouse would count, "one, two, three, four!"

On the count of four his foot would come down hard, and another musical evening would have been launched and would be under full sail in the white cottage by the sea.

Beckie's shrill fife went "tweet, tweet, tweet." Abbie's red drum went "bam, bam, bam!" *Yankee Doodle* was their favorite, but any patriotic marching tune sounded fine to the Bates sisters.

Penelope didn't agree. To avoid the music, she would sit in the garden with only the chill mist rolling in from the sea for company.

The sounds of the evening concerts did not carry into the homes of Scituate. Windows were kept closed against the mist and the chill night air.

But while evenings were quiet in the village, the days were usually filled with excitement.

Beckie and Abbie were the reason for the village uproar. With paper cocked hats on their heads they would march up and down behind the tall sand dunes, in back of the lighthouse. The dunes hid them from sight. They would pretend they were the American Army, the whole American Army, mind you, on the march. They were marching on the hated enemy, the redcoats.

War talk was heard on every side. Beckie and Abbie knew this, of course. They heard people say to each other many times, "We fought and won our war fairly and squarely in the Revolution under General

264

George Washington. Now they want to send their red-coats over again to take our hard-earned liberty away from us."

"Well, we won't stand for this. If we have to, we will fight again for our freedom and independence."

So Beckie and Abbie would march up and down behind the tall dunes, fifing and drumming and playing at being soldiers. Let the redcoats come, the Bates sisters would be ready for them.

War with the redcoats was very close. The people were making patriotic speeches on the village green.

"The redcoats will come as quickly as that," one speaker said, snapping his fingers. "They'll attack us and steal the good food intended for the American Army and Navy. They'll come by sea. Mark you, keep a sharp lookout for them."

All these patriotic speeches made people want to hear stirring marching tunes. Beckie and Abbie's music was in great demand.

Dressed in their best clothing, they played at barn raisings, picnics, and sociables.

"Beckie the fifer and Abbie the drummer will be there," became magic words that were sure to draw a crowd. No one criticized the Bates sisters for being tomboys any more. People cheered and applauded them wildly.

"They sound like the whole American Army on the march," people said, slapping each other on the back.

And when they played *Yankee Doodle,* hats and bonnets were hurled into the air. These were stirring days for Beckie the fifer and Abbie the drummer.

These wonderful times lasted through late summer and autumn. Then the long, cold, New England winter set in. Wind howled around the lighthouse. The sea crashed in angry waves against the shore.

War was really at hand. They were all keeping a sharp lookout for the redcoats now.

Everyone said "Come spring, they'll be here." But it turned out to be a cold wet spring and the enemy did not come.

At last summer arrived. Everyone breathed a sigh of relief. The long New England winter had ended at last. No one thought of sociables and barn raisings even though summer had returned.

And, although Penelope still snoozed beneath the bleeding hearts in the garden, she did not do so to get away from Beckie and Abbie's fifing and drumming. War was too close now. The girls knew that their father would go to fight the redcoats as soon as war was declared. They had no heart for music. The fife and drum hung silently on the wall.

And then one lovely summer day the long-expected news arrived. War had been declared. Every able-bodied man in Scituate responded to the call to the colors. When Mr. Bates broke the news to his family he told them they had to be brave soldiers.

"We must all pitch in and fight for our liberty," he said, as Beckie and Abbie fought back their tears. They knew this was their father's farewell speech before he left them to fight for his country.

"And now I want to give you each a charge to keep," he told them, looking very handsome in his uniform.

"Mother, I leave you in charge of the lighthouse."

"Penelope, you are to be in charge of the lighthouse mice."

"Beckie and Abbie, I place you both in charge of the lighthouse window. Mind now, be brave soldiers, and above all, keep a sharp lookout for the redcoats."

Then he kissed Mrs. Bates and the girls, saluted Penelope, and was gone off to the war.

It was strange how quiet the village became after the men left. People went about their daily duties in silence. Everyone was watching the sea.

Beckie and Abbie had the best spot of all from which to watch it—the lighthouse window.

Everyone awaited news of their loved ones and news of the war. And one day a packet of letters came. Most of the men wrote that American soldiers did not have enough to eat. There was trouble getting supplies through to them. Of course, the redcoats were responsible for this.

Mr. Bates made light of these hardships in his letter, but his wife and daughters could read between the lines. He was hungry, as all American soldiers were. To Penelope he sent a gay message, "Keep a stiff upper lip—soon the war will be over and we'll be having our musical evenings again."

Beckie and Abbie laughed at this. They knew the war had brought a kind of peace to the yellow cat. "I hope you are keeping a sharp lookout for the redcoats," he wrote to the girls.

One day their mother told them word had reached the village that two boatloads of flour were on their way to the American forces. "If they can get as far as Scituate Harbor," Mrs. Bates said, "they will put in until nightfall in the cove beside the lighthouse. Keep a sharp lookout for them. If our men get this flour it could be the turning point in the war.

"The redcoats will be looking for them. The flour barges will stay in the cove till dark. No one knows when they will come."

Flour, their mother explained, was one of the most important things the American forces needed.

"Soldiers cannot keep fighting without proper food," she said. Then she told them what General Washington had said during the Revolution.

"These were his very words, mark you, 'no place in camp is more important to our cause than where bread is made for soldiers.' "

"So watch for the flour boats," Mrs. Bates cautioned them, "they may put in at our cove any day to hide from the redcoats who want to steal the flour. If the boats can hide in the cove until nightfall, they can slip away to Boston under cover of darkness. Then our forces will have good white bread to eat. But don't forget to keep a sharp lookout for the British. They'll be after that flour, you may be sure of that."

So Beckie and Abbie watched the sea from the lighthouse window even more carefully than they had before.

And one morning they saw two barges slip quietly into the cove. "The flour boats are here, the flour boats are here," the girls cried. They were wild with excitement.

The boats were manned by a small crew and hidden snugly in the cove. They were riding at anchor, waiting for dusk.

"If only they can stay until nightfall, all will be well," their mother said. "They've got to hide from the enemy during the day.

"By all means, keep a sharp lookout for the red-coats whatever you do." And Mrs. Bates went down to the kitchen while Beckie and Abbie stayed at the lighthouse window.

It was a long, long day for the girls watching at the window. Even Penelope poked her little yellow nose between them once to see what was going on. Penelope saw only two boats loaded with flour riding at anchor in the cove. There were no mice on the boats she decided, and went to sleep.

When the sun began to sink, Mrs. Bates came up for another look at the sea. Then she again left Beckie and Abbie on guard and went to the kitchen to get supper.

The sun sank lower and lower. Good cooking smells came from the kitchen, but Beckie and Abbie stayed at their post.

The flour boats rode quietly at anchor. Soon the waiting would be over. If only night would come.

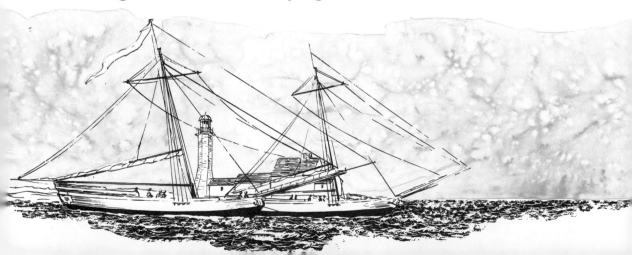

A tiny breeze came up. What appeared to be a toy ship took shape against the horizon. Beckie clutched Abbie's arm. "Look, another ship—two of them now," she whispered. The girls held their breath.

Two ships with sails as red as the sunset came into view.

"They're coming into the harbor under full sail," Beckie cried, "it's the redcoats. Look at their uniforms!"

"Abbie, do you understand? Here come the redcoats. They're coming into the harbor. If they make it to the lighthouse, they'll see the flour barges in the cove."

Abbie leaned far out the window. She was standing on tiptoe. The men's coats were as red as the sinking sun.

"What . . . what shall we do, Beckie?" She looked at her sister with round, frightened eyes.

"I . . . I . . . don't know yet," Beckie replied, "I only know one thing. We've got to get the redcoats out of Scituate Harbor before they see that flour. We've got to save that flour, Abbie. We can't let the British take it away from our men."

"What . . . ?" Abbie started to say, but Beckie stopped her. "Let me think, let me think," she cried as the scarlet-coated men began climbing out of their ships.

"Why, of course! There's only one thing to do. To the dunes, Abbie. Quick—grab your drum. We've got to be real soldiers, now. We've got to fife and drum the red-coats out of Scituate Harbor."

"Run, run, run," cried Beckie suiting her actions to the word, "run and grab your drum off the wall."

"The sand dunes, the sand dunes," Beckie kept shouting, as she plucked her fife off the wall, while Abbie followed at her heels, the red drum bobbing behind her on the cord around her neck.

They raced down the lighthouse stairs, almost falling over Penelope in their mad race to the dunes.

"I . . . I'm afraid of them," Abbie gasped. "They look like giants in those tall hats."

"Run, just run and as soon as we get behind the dunes, start beating that drum. This is no time to be afraid of anything. Begin beating that drum as soon as I start playing *Yankee Doodle*." Beckie dashed ahead, almost falling over her long skirts.

"Well, we made it," Beckie gasped as they reached safety behind the dunes. "We made it, and they didn't see us."

"Now then, one, two, three, four!" Beckie's foot came down on the count of four.

And suddenly Scituate Harbor and all the surrounding countryside was filled with the lively sound of *Yankee Doodle.* The Bates sisters were on the march again, Beckie leading with the fife with Abbie close behind her, beating the drum. Backward and forward they marched behind the sand dunes, their skirts switching in time with the music.

"Tweet, tweet, tweet," and "bam, bam, bam," the Bates sisters were no longer playing at being soldiers. They *were* soldiers . . . a real American Army of Two, fifing and drumming for their country, as the enemy marched toward the lighthouse.

"Halt!" The leader of the redcoats stopped in his tracks. His men stopped also.

"Hark!" he cried. "Hark!"

"*Yankee Doodle came to town,*" sang the fife and drum as the girls marched bravely behind the sand dunes.

A look of astonishment came over the leader of the redcoats as he stood staring toward the dunes.

"Do you men hear all that tootling and thumping?"

"Blimey, yes," cried a voice from the ranks.

"Sounds like the whole American Army has come up from Boston to protect their flour."

"Retreat men, back to the ships. The Americans are behind those tall dunes. Heaven knows how many of them are there."

"Retreat, man the ships!" cried the commanding officer.

Never was an order carried out more promptly. The redcoats fell over each other to get back to their ships.

They did not even glance in the direction of the flour boats riding quietly at anchor in the cove.

The music behind the dunes continued as the redcoats fled in terror under full sail.

They would have been amazed to learn that the American Army that had outsmarted them consisted of two little girls in pigtails.

Beckie and Abbie continued to fife and drum behind the dunes until they were sure the enemy soldiers were out of sight.

Then, when they stole from behind their protecting shelter, they saw two boats, loaded with flour, slip quietly out of Scituate Harbor and make for Boston. Their precious cargo was on its way to the American forces under cover of the protecting night.

The Bates sisters had been as brave and heroic as any soldier or sailor could have been. Their country would never forget what they had done for it.

But now they were just two hungry little girls making their way back to the white cottage in the dusk.

Their mother, who had seen everything that happened from the lighthouse window, met them with open arms.

"I'm so proud of you, so very proud of you," she told them, hugging them to her.

"Whatever made you think of doing what you did?" she asked them when supper was over.

"Why, we just played soldiers and marched again," Beckie replied. "Only this time we were not pretending."

"Well, I guess my brave army of two had better march to bed," Mrs. Bates said. "To bed, to bed, get your nightcaps on."

And away went Beckie and Abbie to their little beds. Only this time they were followed by Penelope, who had hidden from the redcoats beneath the flowers in the garden.

Two sleepy and tired girls went to bed and awakened to discover that overnight they had become famous. And to this day, they are still famous.

They are still known as the American Army of Two, who fifed and drummed the redcoats out of Scituate Harbor and saved two boatloads of flour for American soldiers and sailors who were fighting for our country's independence and liberty.

Only a short time after this, the War of 1812 ended in victory for the United States. Americans did not fear the redcoats ever again.

Beckie and Abbie's father was among the first to arrive when the men of Scituate came marching home from the war.

Mr. Bates had heard of his daughters' fame even in Boston.

"I told you you'd be proud of Beckie and Abbie's fifing and drumming some day," he told his wife.

Mrs. Bates smiled happily. "You said they played stirring music and they proved that."

"They surely stirred up the British," her husband chuckled.

"They ran when we played *Yankee Doodle*," Abbie told her father.

"Well," Mr. Bates looked at his wife from the corner of his eye, "are Beckie and Abbie going to take up fancy work like the other girls now, or do we go back to musical evenings?"

"Of course, we go back to musical evenings," Mrs. Bates replied. "I wouldn't think of having it any other way."

Whereupon the tootling and thumping rang through Scituate again as the musical evenings got under way. But no one ever thought of complaining, even when the girls marched and fifed and drummed outdoors.

The sociables and barn raisings started again and the Bates sisters were always the main attraction.

This went on for many, many happy years, for Beckie and Abbie lived happily to ripe old ages.

There is proof that this took place right in Scituate Harbor. The lighthouse is still there as well as the little cottage. On the cottage, beside the door, is a bronze plaque that says that this was the home of Rebecca and Abigail Bates, the two girls who fifed and drummed the British redcoats out of the harbor during the War of 1812.

And in Old South Church in the city of Boston, you may hear the story of the famous Bates sisters told again.

In the church you may see two letters . . . letters in Beckie and Abbie's own handwritings.

The letters tell how the girls formed the American Army of Two and marched with fife and drum behind the sand dunes, scaring the redcoats and chasing them away.

Faded yellow letters they are now, and their ink is dim with age.

There is no mistake about the names, though, for they are there for everyone to read, "Rebecca Bates, fifer. Abigail Bates, drummer."

—Harriet Evatt

What Do You Think?

1. Why do you suppose fifes and drums were used in the army in 1812?

2. If you had lived in 1812, how do you think you would have felt if you had seen enemy ships coming to capture the flour?

3. What other ways could Beckie and Abbie have tried to save the flour?

Taking A Closer Look

1. In the Bates family, who worked at the lighthouse?

2. What was Penelope's job?

3. How did Penelope react to the music of the fife and drum?

4. Why were the Redcoats in Scituate Harbor?

5. Why did the American army need the flour?

6. Why did Beckie and Abbie's playing scare off the Redcoats?

7. How did their father feel when he heard the news?

281

A Touch of Magic
A Touch of Wonder

Air and seas and skies belong to everyone. So do folk tales. If you could travel to every country in the world, you would hear some stories over and over again. People of every country love tales of magic, and tales of wonder. For just this little while, join the millions who have listened to these tales—and let the magic and the wonder of "make-believe" touch you!

Every dragon is terrible. Vasil[1] *knew* that. But still he promised to try to kill this dragon. What kind of magic did he know? None. What extra-special strength did he have? None. What armies did he have to help him? None. Then what *did* he have? Well . . . just a club—and—you'll see the rest!

[1] Vasil (vah-SEEL)

284

How Vasil Vanquished the Dragon

Whether it was so or not, whether it is true or false, let us hear what the tale has to tell. And so here it is.

To a certain land there once came a most fearful and terrible Dragon. He dug himself out a deep hole by a mountain in the midst of a forest, and lay down to rest.

Whether he rested long or not no one now recalls, but the moment he rose he shouted loudly for all to hear:

"Come, folk, men and women, old and young, you must each of you bring me a tribute every day: one of you can bring me a cow, another — a lamb, and a third — a pig! He who obeys, will live. But he who does not, will die, for him I will devour!"

The people were frightened, and they began paying the Dragon the tribute he asked for. This went on for a long time till at last there came a day when there was nothing left to bring, for they had all become extremely poor. But the Dragon was of the kind that could not let a day pass without gorging himself. So he began flying from village to village, seizing people and carrying them off to his den.

The people went about wailing like lost souls, vainly trying to find a way to deliver themselves from the cruel Dragon.

Now at that very time a man named Vasil came to those parts, and he found that the people went about sad and disheartened, wringing their hands and weeping loudly.

"What is the trouble?" asked he. "Why are you all weeping?"

The people told him of their trouble, and Vasil tried to comfort them.

"Calm yourselves," said he. "I will try to save you from the Dragon."

And taking a heavy cudgel, he went to the forest where the Dragon lived.

The Dragon saw him, and rolling his great green eyes, asked:

"Why have you come here with that cudgel?"

"To give you a beating!" Vasil replied.

"My, how brave you are!" said the Dragon. "You had better run away while you still can. For I only have to blow once, and you will be blown clean away from here, a full three *versts!*"[1]

Vasil smiled.

"Don't you boast, you old scarecrow," said he. "I've seen worse monsters than you! We'll see which of us can blow the harder. Go on, blow!"

[1] *versts* (VERSTS)

286

And the Dragon blew so hard that the leaves rained down from the trees, and Vasil was thrown to his knees.

"Ha, that's nothing!" said he, springing to his feet. "Why, it's enough to make a cat laugh! Now let me try. Only first you must bandage your eyes if you don't want them to jump out of their sockets."

The Dragon tied a kerchief over his eyes, and Vasil came up and struck him such a blow on the head with his cudgel that sparks poured from the Dragon's eyes.

"Can it be that you are stronger than I?" the Dragon asked. "Let's try again and see which of us is fastest at crushing a rock."

And the Dragon seized a rock weighing all of a hundred *poods*[1] and squeezed it with his claws so hard that the dust rose up in clouds.

"There's nothing to that!" laughed Vasil. "Let's see you squeeze it so that the water will run from it."

[1] *poods* (POODS)

287

The Dragon was frightened. He was beginning to feel that Vasil was the stronger of the two, and glancing at Vasil's cudgel, said:

"Ask of me what you will, and you shall have it."

"I don't need anything," Vasil replied. "I have plenty of everything in the house, more than you have."

"Can that be true?" asked the Dragon in disbelief.

"If you don't believe me, come and see for yourself!"

So they got into a cart and drove off.

By now the Dragon was becoming very hungry. He saw a herd of bullocks on the edge of a forest and he said to Vasil:

"Go and catch a bullock and we'll have a bite to eat."

And Vasil went to the forest and began stripping bast from the lime-trees. The Dragon waited and waited, and at last went to look for him.

"What is taking you so long?" he asked him.

"Can't you see I am stripping bast from the lime-trees," Vasil replied.

"What do you need bast for?"

"To make some rope so as to catch us five bullocks for dinner."

"What do we need five bullocks for? One is enough."

And the Dragon caught a bullock by the nape of its neck and dragged it to the cart.

"Now go and bring us some wood to roast the bullock," said he to Vasil.

And Vasil sat down under an oak tree in the forest, closed his eyes, and chuckled to himself.

The Dragon waited for him for a long time, and at last, losing patience, went to look for him.

"What is taking you so long?" he asked him.

"I want to take a dozen oaks or so, so I'm trying to pick the thickest among them."

"What do we want with a dozen oaks? One oak is enough," said the Dragon, and giving one powerful tug, he pulled out the thickest of the oaks.

He roasted the bullock and invited Vasil to join him.

"Go ahead and eat it yourself," said Vasil. "I'll have something at home. What's one bullock for me—just a bite!"

The Dragon ate the bullock and licked his lips. They rode on and soon came to Vasil's house. The children saw their father coming from a distance, and they cried out joyously:

"Father's coming! Father's coming!"

But the Dragon did not catch the words and asked:

"What are the children shouting?"

"They are pleased that I am bringing you home for their dinner. They're very hungry."

By now the Dragon was badly frightened, so he jumped from the cart and took to his heels. But he missed the road and landed in a bog. The bog was very deep, so deep indeed that the bottom could not be reached, and the Dragon sank down, down, down, and was drowned. And so that was the end of him.

—*Russian Folk Tale*
Translated by Irina Zheleznova

What Do You Think?

1. How is the Dragon the same as other dragons you may have read about? How is he different?

2. How was Vasil able to make the Dragon become so frightened? What did you think of Vasil's plan?

3. Why was Vasil the only one in the land brave enough to try to rid the people of the Dragon? Would you like to have someone like Vasil for a friend? Why?

Taking A Closer Look

1. What did the Dragon ask the people to bring to him as a tribute?

2. How did the Dragon force them to do as he asked?

3. When there were no animals left, what did the Dragon eat?

4. Explain how Vasil first planned to save the people from the Dragon.

5. How did the Dragon show his strength?

6. When the Dragon saw Vasil's children, what mistake did he make?

7. What finally happened to the Dragon?

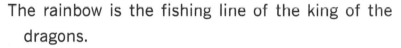

The rainbow is the fishing line of the king of the
  dragons.
The king of the dragons sits in the high places
  above the earth,
in places where no man has ever been.
He fishes in the waters below the earth;
and the rainbow is his fishing line.

—from Malaya

Who's the smartest animal in all
the world? Ask the Coyote—and
he'll tell you, "*I* am, of course!"
When is a half-hour *not* a half-
hour? Ask the Fox—and he'll
grin and chuckle and say, "Ask
Señor Coyote[1]. He knows *everything.*" See if you agree that
Señor Coyote is the smartest
animal in all the world.

[1] Señor Coyote (say-NYOR kigh-OH-tee)

Señor Coyote and Señor Fox

Almost everyone in Mexico knows that Señor Coyote is so smart that he is more or less of a magician. There are very few animals, and no people in all the world, that can do some of the things that Señor Coyote can do. And yet, with all his smartness, this smartest of all creatures, Señor Coyote, is often made a fool of by creatures smaller than himself. Why this is so would be hard to explain unless it could be said that Señor Coyote does not think his fellow animals have as much cleverness as they really have.

One day Señor Coyote was traveling through the country towards a big something that stood up on the level plain like a great cathedral. As he approached it, however, he could see plainly that it was a tall rock cliff more than three hundred feet high, standing alone in the middle of the desert.

Señor Coyote arrived at this great cliff and began to walk around it; and as he made a turn around one corner of it, whom should he see lying dozing in the sun but little Señor Fox.

"Aha, my friend Brother Fox," said Señor Coyote.

"And so near dinnertime too." But even as Señor Coyote was thinking of eating up little Señor Fox, this quick little animal was on his feet pushing against the high sheer side of the cliff with all his might.

"Quick!" he shouted. "Help me hold up this cliff! It is falling over and will crush us. *Andale, pronto!*[1] Brother Coyote."

It is plain to see that Señor Fox had thought up his plan very quickly. Señor Fox never sleeps with both eyes shut. He has always got one wide open, looking out for trouble. Half the night he sleeps with one eye open, and the other half with the other open. The same for his ears; they both take turns keeping watch while he sleeps. This is perhaps the reason that Señor Fox saw Señor Coyote before Señor Coyote saw him. And now he was straining and pushing against the cliff wall, his feet scrambling on the ground, shouting for Señor Coyote to come to his side and help him keep the cliff from falling down.

At first Señor Coyote was a bit wary and thought certainly that Señor Fox was trying to play some trick on him. But he was standing right next to the cliff, and when he looked up at the top, it did seem that the great tall cliff was slowly toppling over onto him. So with one spring, he was at Señor Fox's side, pushing with all his might.

[1] *Andale, pronto* (AHN-dah-lay PRON-toh)

296

"That was a narrow escape," panted Señor Fox. "If you hadn't happened along, this rock would have fallen over and crushed me."

Señor Coyote looked up again at the top of the cliff and as he did, it seemed to start falling slowly over towards them. Quickly he ducked his head and began pushing so quickly and with such force that the gravel flew under his feet.

"This is terrible," said Señor Fox in a complaining voice. "We will have to stay here now until perhaps forever."

"Yes," said Señor Coyote, "we must stay here till help comes. If we try to get away from here, the cliff will fall on us before we can run out of danger."

Suddenly Señor Fox spoke with the cheerfulness of someone who has just thought of a way out of some terrible trouble.

"I know what we can do," he almost sang.

"What, then?" gasped Señor Coyote, blowing a drop of sweat off the end of his nose.

"I will run for help while you stay here and hold up the cliff," said Señor Fox, smiling.

"Oh, no," said Señor Coyote, not too pleasantly. "No, you don't. It takes both of us to hold this thing up. You will stay here, Brother Fox."

"Why?" said Señor Fox. "If I held it up for a while by myself, then surely you, with your great strength, can hold it up for the short time it will take me to run and bring help, and chickens and *tortillas*.[1] I will bring others with me and they will be carrying poles to

[1] *tortillas* (tor-TEE-yahz)

298

brace this thing up with. Otherwise we will both stay here until we grow into the shape we are now in, with our hands against the face of this rock. Perhaps our feet will grow roots so deep into the ground that no one can pull us out."

To this Señor Coyote said nothing, but seemed to be thinking.

"What do you say?" asked Señor Fox. "How about it, Brother Coyote? I won't be gone more than half an hour."

Señor Coyote shook his head slowly and then said, "All right then; I guess I am somewhat stronger than I think I am. But do not be gone too long, Brother Fox."

"Of course not," said Señor Fox, easing carefully away from the cliff. "*Adiós!*[1] Brother Coyote."

"Remember," said Señor Coyote pushing harder against the cliff, "half an hour, Brother Fox."

Señor Fox was gone, lightly loping over the prairie, with a final word called over his shoulder, "Push harder, harder, Brother Coyote. You must make up for both of us, you know."

[1] *Adiós* (ah-DYOS)

And so push harder Señor Coyote did. He pushed until it seemed that his arms would drop off, they ached so badly. It was at these times when his arms were tired that he would steal a quick glance up at the great face of rock extending up to the blue sky, to see if perhaps the cliff had gotten out of the notion of falling.

But no. Every time Señor Coyote looked up there, the cliff seemed to be starting to topple. So with a quick movement and a grunt or two, Señor Coyote would dig his feet into the ground and groan and strain and push. And every time he did this, the rocks and dirt would spurt backwards from his churning feet.

A half an hour passed and no Señor Fox. An hour passed and then two. Señor Coyote was up to his knees now in a hole he had dug with his feet; and he was calling and singing in his own Coyote voice for Señor Fox to return. The sun sank below the desert mountains and darkness came. Up came the moon, round and silvery-bright, shining down on Señor Coyote whimpering, shivering, and yelling for Señor Fox or for anyone at all.

All night he stood there howling and suffering, Señor Coyote did. And imagine, if you can, when daylight came, how there stood Señor Coyote almost up to his hips in the hole he had dug.

Looking desperately over his shoulder, he said, "I cannot hold out much longer. I wonder what has happened to Brother Fox." Up at the cliff he dared not look.

"I will make a break for my life," he said. "I will not last much longer here anyhow. I am about to starve to death."

So, making one last push against the cliff with about all the strength left in his arms, Señor Coyote leapt out of the hole and without looking up, ran straight out on the plain away from the cliff. As he ran, of course he thought that at any moment the cliff might be on top of him. So fast he went that his legs could not be seen. He looked like some wingless bird flying like the wind close to the ground.

Not until he was at least a half a mile away from the high rock did Señor Coyote turn and look back, expecting to see the tremendous rock come thundering to earth in a huge cloud of dust. But wonder of wonders, there stood the big rock upright and unchanged. Señor Coyote could only stare.

"It cannot be," he said. "It is impossible."

Then the truth dawned upon him. Señor Fox had simply made a fool of him. That was all there was to it. He was so angry that he jumped up in the air and came down chasing his tail around and around while his barks echoed across the desert to the mountains. And Señor Fox, where was he? *Quién sabe?*[1] (Who knows?)

—*Mexican Folk Tale*
Dan Storm

[1] *Quién sabe* (kyen SAH-bay)

What Do You Think?

1. Why do you think it was possible for Señor Fox to play such a trick on Señor Coyote?

2. How did Señor Coyote feel when he realized Señor Fox had tricked him? How would you feel if someone played a trick like that on you?

3. Why was Señor Fox such a trickster?

4. What lesson might Señor Coyote have learned from his experience with Señor Fox?

Taking A Closer Look

1. What was the "something" that Señor Fox told Señor Coyote he was holding up?

2. Why didn't Señor Coyote seriously suspect Señor Fox of trying to play a trick on him?

3. How did Señor Fox convince Señor Coyote to hold up the cliff while Señor Fox went for help?

4. What did Señor Coyote do after Señor Fox had left?

5. Why did Señor Coyote finally give up trying to "hold up the cliff"?

Coyote

I hear coyote calling in the nighttime.
Calling me, his brother, in the moonlight.
He guards the scattered hogans on the desert.
No harm will touch me. Coyote is my sentry.
I close my eyes and sleep until the morning.

—*Patricia Miles Martin*

"Who has seen the wind?
Neither you nor I." But once
there was a boy who did—and
he talked to the wind—and the
wind talked to him! And then
what? Oh, *ever so much* more.
But as the boy's mother said,
"Seeing is believing."

The Boy Who Went to the North Wind

Once on a time there was an old widow who had one son. Since she was poorly and weak, her son had to go up into the storehouse to fetch meal for cooking. When he got outside the storehouse, and was just going down the steps, along came the North Wind, puffing and blowing. The North Wind caught up the meal, and was away with it through the air. Then the boy went back into the storehouse for more. But when he came out again on the steps, if the North Wind didn't come again and carry off the meal with a puff! And more than that, the North Wind did so the third time. At this the boy got very angry. And as he was thinking how hard it was that the North Wind should behave so, he decided he'd just look him up, and ask him to give back his meal.

So off he went. But the way was long, and he walked and walked. At last he came to the North Wind's house.

"Good day," said the boy, "and thank you for coming to see us yesterday."

"Good day," shouted the North Wind for his voice was hard and gruff. "And thanks for coming to see me. What do you want?"

"Oh!" answered the boy. "I only wished to ask you to be so good as to let me have back that meal you took from me on the storehouse steps. We haven't much to live on now. And if you're to go on snapping up the little bit we have, there'll be nothing for us to do but to starve."

"I haven't got your meal," said the North Wind. "But if you are in such need, I'll give you a cloth which will get you everything you want. All you have to do is say, 'Cloth, spread yourself, and serve up all kinds of good dishes!' "

With this the boy was well content. But, as the way was so long that he couldn't get home in one day, he turned into an inn on the way. When everyone was going to sit down to supper, he laid the cloth on a table which stood in the corner, and he said,—

"Cloth, spread yourself, and serve up all kinds of good dishes!"

He had scarcely said the words before the cloth did as it was bid. All who stood by thought it a fine thing, most of all the innkeeper. So, when all were fast asleep, at dead of night, he took the cloth, and put another in its place, just like the one the boy had got from the North Wind. But this one couldn't so much as serve up a bit of dry bread.

So, when the boy woke, he took his cloth and went off with it. And that day he went home to his mother.

"Now," said he, "I've been to the North Wind's house, and a good fellow he is, for he gave me this cloth. When I only say to it, 'Cloth, spread yourself, and serve up all kinds of good dishes,' I get any sort of food."

"All very true, I'm sure," said his mother, "but seeing is believing. I shan't believe it till I see it."

So the boy made haste, drew out a table, laid the cloth on it, and said,—

"Cloth, spread yourself, and serve up all kinds of good dishes!"

But never a bit of dry bread did the cloth serve up.

"Well," said the boy, "there's no help for it but to go to the North Wind again." And away he went.

So, late in the afternoon, he came to where the North Wind lived.

"Good evening!" said the boy.

"Good evening!" said the North Wind.

"I want my rights for that meal of ours which you took," said the boy. "And as for that cloth I got, it isn't worth a penny."

"I've got no meal," said the North Wind; "but yonder you have a ram which makes nothing but golden coins as soon as you say to it, —

" 'Ram, ram! Make money!' "

So the boy thought this a fine thing. Then once again, as it was too far to get home that day, he turned in for the night at the same inn where he had slept before.

Before he called for anything, he tried the truth of what the North Wind had said of the ram, and found it was really true. But when the innkeeper saw that, he thought it was a famous ram, and, when the boy had fallen asleep, the innkeeper took another ram which wouldn't make gold coins and changed the two.

Next morning off went the boy. When he got home to his mother, he said, —

"After all, the North Wind is a jolly fellow. For now he has given me a ram which can make gold coins if I only say, 'Ram, ram! Make money!' "

310

"All very true, I'm sure," said his mother, "but I shan't believe any such stuff until I see the coins made."

"Ram, ram! Make money!" said the boy. But if the ram made anything it wasn't money.

So the boy went back again to the North Wind. He told him the ram was worth nothing and said he must have his rights for the meal.

"Well," said the North Wind. "I've nothing else to give you but that old stick in the corner yonder. But it's such a wonderful stick that if you say,—

" 'Stick, stick! Lay on!' It lays on till you say,—

" 'Stick, stick! Now stop!' "

So, as the way was long, the boy turned in this night again at the same inn. Since he could pretty well guess how things stood with the cloth and ram, he lay down at once on the bench and began to snore as if he were asleep.

Now the innkeeper, who easily saw that the stick must be worth something, hunted up one which was like it and when he heard the boy snore, was going to change the two, but just as the innkeeper was about to take it, the boy bawled out, —

"Stick, stick! Lay on."

So the stick began to beat the innkeeper, till he jumped over chairs, and tables, and benches, and yelled and roared, —

"Oh my! Oh my! Bid the stick be still. Then you shall have back both your cloth and your ram."

When the boy thought the innkeeper had got enough, he said, —

"Stick, stick! Now stop."

Then he took the cloth and put it into his pocket, and went home with his stick in his hand, leading the ram by a cord round its horns. And so he got his rights for the meal he had lost.

—Norse Folk Tale
Translated by Sir George Webbe Dasent

What Do You Think?

1. What kind of meal do you think the North Wind blew away?

2. Why do you suppose the North Wind kept giving the boy one gift after another?

3. How did you feel when the innkeeper was forced to give back the cloth and the ram?

Taking A Closer Look

1. What was the first gift that the North Wind gave the boy?

2. What did the innkeeper do with this gift?

3. On the boy's next visit, what gift did the North Wind give him?

4. Why did the innkeeper steal the second gift?

5. What was the last gift the North Wind gave the boy?

6. How did the last gift help the boy get back his cloth and ram?

The Wind is a man with a spade in his hand.
He stands above the earth and shovels the winds.
He shovels the winds into the South,
and the winds that blow into the North.
He shovels the winds to the East and to the West.

—from Lapland

Over the wintry
forest, winds howl in a rage
with no leaves to blow.

—*Soseki*

When a tiger sighs and cries—
and lies—watch out! When a tree
and a road *talk*—sit and listen
and wonder! But when you meet
a jackal—get ready to laugh—
and laugh—and laugh—and . . .

The Tiger, the Brahman, and the Jackal

Once upon a time, a tiger was caught in a trap. He tried in vain to get out through the bars, and rolled and bit with rage and grief when he failed.

By chance a poor Brahman came by. "O holy man, let me out of this cage," cried the tiger.

"No, my friend," replied the Brahman mildly, "you would probably eat me if I did."

"Not at all!" promised the tiger. "If you would only let me out of this cage, I should be forever grateful, and serve you as a slave!"

When the tiger sobbed and sighed and wept, the Brahman's heart softened. At last he agreed to open the door of the cage. Out popped the tiger, and, seizing the poor man, cried, "What a fool you are! What is to prevent me from eating you now? I have been shut up so long I am terribly hungry!"

The Brahman pleaded for his life. At first the tiger would not listen to his pleas. But finally the tiger promised to let the Brahman go unharmed on just one condition. He must find three things that would agree that the tiger was unjust.

The Brahman accepted the condition gladly.

First, the Brahman told his story to a *pipal*[1] tree. He asked what the tree thought of the matter. The *pipal* tree replied coldly: "I give shade and shelter to every one who passes by. In return they only tear down my branches to feed their cattle. What have you to complain about?"

Then the Brahman, sad at heart, went farther until he saw a buffalo turning a water wheel. After hearing his story, the buffalo felt no pity for the Brahman either,

[1] *pipal* (PEE-pǝl)

but answered: "You are a fool to expect gratitude. Look at me. When I gave milk, they fed me cotton seed and oil cake. Now that I have no milk to give, they tie me here, and feed me garbage."

The Brahman, sadder still, asked the road to give him its opinion.

"My dear sir," said the road, "how foolish you are to expect anything else. Here I am, useful to everybody. Yet all, rich and poor, great and small, trample on me as they go past. They give me nothing in return but the ashes of their pipes and the husks of their grain!"

Then the Brahman turned back sorrowfully. On the way he met a jackal, who called out: "What's the matter, Mr. Brahman? You look as miserable as a fish out of water!"

The Brahman told him all that had happened.

"How very confusing!" said the jackal, when the Brahman had finished his story. "Would you mind telling me over again, for everything has become so mixed up?"

The Brahman told his tale all over again, but the jackal still shook his head as if he could not understand.

"It's very odd," said the jackal. "It all seems to go in one ear and out the other! I will go to the place where it all happened. Perhaps then I shall be able to decide whether the tiger was unjust."

They returned to the cage. The tiger was waiting beside it for the Brahman, sharpening his teeth and claws.

"You've been away a long time!" growled the savage beast, "but now let us begin our dinner."

"*Our* dinner!" thought the miserable Brahman, as his knees knocked together with fright. "What a delicate way of putting it!"

"Give me five minutes, my lord!" he pleaded. "I would like to explain matters to the jackal here. He is somewhat slow to understand."

The tiger agreed, and the Brahman began the whole story over again. He didn't miss a single detail, spinning as long a tale as possible.

"Oh, my poor brain, my poor brain!" cried the jackal, wringing his paws. "Let me see. How did it all begin? You were in the cage, and the tiger came walking by—"

"Pooh," interrupted the tiger, "what a fool you are! *I* was in the cage."

"Of course!" cried the jackal, pretending to tremble with fright. "Oh yes! I was in the cage—no I wasn't— dear! dear! Where are my brains? Let me see—the tiger was in the Brahman, and the cage came walking by. No, that's not it, either! Well, don't mind me, but begin your dinner, for I shall never understand!"

"Yes, you shall!" returned the tiger, in a rage at the jackal's stupidity; "I'll *make* you understand! Look here—I am the tiger—"

"Yes, my lord!"

"And that is the Brahman—"

"Yes, my lord!"

"And that is the cage—"

"Yes, my lord!"

"And *I* was in the cage—do you understand?"

"Yes—no— Please, my lord—"

"Well?" cried the tiger impatiently.

"Please, my lord!—how did you get in?"

"How! —why in the usual way, of course!"

"Oh, dear me!—my head is beginning to whirl again! Please don't be angry, my lord, but what *is* the usual way?"

At this the tiger lost patience. Jumping into the cage he cried: "*This* way! Now do you understand how it was?"

"Perfectly!" grinned the jackal, as he quickly shut the door, "and if you will permit me to say so, I think matters will remain just as they were!"

322   —Indian Folk Tale

What Do You Think?

1. What did you think when the Brahman let the tiger out of the cage?

2. Why didn't the tree, the buffalo, and the road take the Brahman's side? Do you think they were right?

3. How was the jackal like Señor Fox? Do you think Vasil was a trickster too? Tell why or why not.

Taking A Closer Look

1. Why did the Brahman let the tiger out of the cage?

2. How did the tiger say he would act when he was free?

3. What did the tiger tell the Brahman he would have to find before he would let the Brahman go free?

4. How did the jackal help the Brahman?

5. Explain how the jackal was able to trick the tiger.

India

They hunt, the velvet tigers in the jungle,
The spotted jungle full of shapeless patches—
Sometimes they're leaves, sometimes they're hanging
  flowers,
Sometimes they're hot gold patches of the sun:
They hunt, the velvet tigers in the jungle!

The grass is flaming and the trees are growing,
The mud is gurgling in the pools,
Green toads are watching, crimson parrots are flying,
Two pairs of eyes meet one another glowing—
They hunt, the velvet tigers in the jungle!

—*W. J. Turner*

Did you ever hear of a *royal sneeze?* Then listen! This king's sneeze is a matter of life and death. Really. It all happens when an angry king can't force or bribe "the shepherd with the bright blue eyes" to obey him.

To Your Good Health

Long, long ago there lived a king who was such a mighty ruler that whenever he sneezed everyone in the whole country had to say, "To your good health!" Everyone said it except the shepherd with the bright, blue eyes, and he would not say it.

The king heard of this and was very angry. He sent for the shepherd to appear before him.

The shepherd came and stood before the throne, where the king sat looking very grand and powerful. But however grand or powerful he might be, the shepherd did not feel a bit afraid of him.

"Say at once, 'To my good health!' " cried the king.

"To my good health!" replied the shepherd.

"To *mine* — to *mine*, you rascal!" stormed the king.

"To mine, to mine, Your Majesty," was the answer.

"But to *mine* — to my *own*," roared the king and beat his chest in a rage.

"Well, yes; to mine, of course, to my own," cried the shepherd and gently tapped his breast.

The king was beside himself with fury. He did not know what to do.

Then the Lord Chamberlain whispered to the shepherd, "Say at once—say this very moment: 'To your good health, Your Majesty.' For if you don't say it, you'll lose your life."

"No, I won't say it till I can have the princess for my wife," answered the shepherd.

Now the princess was sitting on a little throne beside the king, her father. She looked as sweet and lovely as a little golden dove. When she heard what the shepherd said she could not help laughing, for this young shepherd pleased her very much. Indeed, he pleased her better than any king's son she had ever seen.

But the king was not so pleasant as his daughter. He gave order to throw the shepherd at once into the white bear's pit. The guards led him away and thrust him into the pit. Now the white bear had eaten nothing for two days, so he was very hungry.

The door of the pit had hardly closed when the bear rushed at the shepherd. But when it saw his eyes, it was so frightened it was ready to eat itself. It shrank away into a corner and gazed at him from there. Even though it was starving, it did not dare touch him. Instead, it nibbled its own paws from sheer hunger.

328

The shepherd was afraid that if he once took his eyes off the beast, he would be a dead man. To keep himself awake, he made songs and sang them. And so the night went by.

Next morning the Lord Chamberlain came, expecting to see the shepherd's bones. He was amazed to find him alive and well. He led him to the king who fell into a furious rage and said:

"Well, you have learned what it is to be very near death. Now will you say, 'To my good health?' "

But the shepherd answered, "I am not afraid of ten deaths! I will only say it if I may have the princess for my wife."

"Then go to your death!" cried the king, and ordered him to be thrown into the den with the wild boars.

The wild boars had not been fed for a week, so when the shepherd was thrust into their den, they rushed at him to tear him to pieces. But the shepherd took a little flute out of the sleeve of his jacket and began to play a merry tune. Hearing it, the wild boars first of all shrank shyly away. Then they got up on their hind legs and danced gaily.

The shepherd would have given anything to be able to laugh, they looked so funny. But he did not dare stop playing, for he knew that the moment he stopped, they would pounce on him and tear him to pieces. His eyes were useless to him in the den, for he could not have stared ten wild boars in the face at once. So he kept on playing and the wild boars danced very slowly, as if in a minuet. Then by degrees, he played faster and faster till they could hardly twist and turn. Finally they ended by falling all over each other in a heap, exhausted and out of breath.

Then at last the shepherd dared to laugh. He laughed so long and so loud that when the Lord Chamberlain came early in the morning, expecting to find only his bones, the shepherd's tears were still running down his cheeks from laughter.

As soon as the king was dressed, the shepherd was again brought before him. But he was more angry than ever to think the wild boars had not torn the man to bits, and he said:

"Well, you have learned how it feels to be near ten deaths. Now say, 'To my good health!' "

But the shepherd still replied, "I do not fear a hundred deaths. I will say it only if I may have the princess for my wife."

"Then go to a hundred deaths!" roared the king. And this time, he ordered the shepherd to be thrown down into the deep well of swords.

The guards dragged him away to a dark dungeon. In the middle of it there was a deep well with sharp swords all round it. At the bottom of the well was a little light which would show whether anyone thrown into the well had fallen to the bottom.

When the shepherd was dragged to the dungeon, he begged the guards to leave him alone a little while so that he could look down into the pit of swords. Perhaps he might after all make up his mind to say "To your good health" to the king.

So the guards left him alone. Immediately, he stood his long stick near the well, hung his cloak round the stick, and put his hat on top. He also hung his knapsack up inside the cloak so that it would seem to have somebody inside it. Then he called out to the guards. He told them he had considered the matter, but he still could not make up his mind to say what the king wished.

The guards came in, threw the hat, cloak, knapsack, and stick, all down the well together. They watched until they saw the light at the bottom of the well go out. Then, they left, thinking that they had finally seen the end of the shepherd. But he had hidden in a dark corner, where he was laughing to himself all the time.

Quite early next morning, the Lord Chamberlain came, carrying a lamp. He nearly fell backward with surprise when he saw the shepherd alive and well. He brought him once more to the king. Enraged more than ever, the king cried:

"Well, now that you have been near a hundred deaths, will you say, 'To your good health'?"

But the shepherd only gave the same answer. "I won't say it till the princess is my wife."

"Perhaps after all you may do it for less," said the king. He saw that there was no chance of doing away with the shepherd, so he ordered the state coach to be made ready. Then he had the shepherd get in with him and sit beside him. Next he ordered the coachman to drive to the silver forest. When they reached it he said:

"Do you see this forest? Well, if you will say, 'To your good health,' I will give it to you."

The shepherd turned hot and cold by turns, but he still persisted, "I will not say it till the princess is my wife."

The king was very much vexed. He drove farther on till they came to a splendid castle, all gold, and then he said:

"Do you see this golden castle? Well, I will give you that too, the silver forest and the golden castle, if only you will say that one thing to me, 'To your good health.'"

The shepherd gaped and wondered and was quite dazzled, but still he said, "No, I will not say it till I have the princess for my wife."

This time the king was overwhelmed with grief, and gave orders to drive on to the diamond pond. There he tried once more.

"Do you see this diamond pond? I will give you that too, the silver forest and the golden castle and the diamond pond. You shall have them all—all—if you will but say, 'To your good health!'"

The shepherd had to shut his eyes tight so he would not be dazzled with the brilliant pond, but still he said, "No, no; I will not say it till I have the princess for my wife."

Then the king saw that all his efforts were useless, and that he might as well give in. Sighing he said, "Well, well, it's all the same to me—I will give you my daughter for your wife. But, then, you really and truly must say to me, 'To your good health.'"

"Of course I'll say it. Why should I not say it? It stands to reason that I shall say it then."

At this the king was more delighted than anyone could have believed. He made it known all through the country that there were to be great rejoicings, for the princess was going to be married. Everyone rejoiced to think that the princess, who had refused so many royal suitors, should have ended by falling in love with the blue-eyed shepherd.

Never before had such a wedding been seen! Everyone ate and drank and danced. Even the sick were feasted, and all newborn children were given presents.

But the greatest merry-making was in the king's palace. There the best bands played and the best food was cooked. A huge crowd of people sat down to table, and all was fun and laughter.

According to custom, a great boar's head was carried in on a big dish and placed before the king to carve. The savory smell was so strong that the king began to sneeze with all his might.

"To your very good health," cried the shepherd before anyone else. And the king was so delighted that he did not regret he had given the shepherd his daughter.

In time, when the old king died, the shepherd succeeded him. He made a very good king and never expected his people to wish him well against their wills. But, all the same, everyone *did* wish him well, for they all loved him.

—*Russian Folk Tale*

What Do You Think?

1. Why was the king terribly upset when the shepherd refused to say, "To your good health!"? Did he have good reason to feel this way?

2. Why do you suppose the shepherd pleased the princess more than any of the princes she had met?

3. Why do you think the people thought the shepherd made such a good king?

Taking A Closer Look

1. What did the shepherd want before he would agree to say "To your good health"?

2. How did the king try to force the shepherd to say "To your good health"?

3. What bribes did the king offer the shepherd to say "To your good health"?

4. How do you know the shepherd made a good king?

The Case of the
Elevator Duck

Polly Berrien Berends

1

A DUCK OUT OF WATER

On weekends and evenings and vacations I am a detective. I do not wear a disguise. I do not need disguises because I am only eleven years old. Nobody suspects an eleven-year-old boy of being a detective. My name is Gilbert. I live in a housing project. I live in 12H.

Someday I am going to be a full-time detective. So for now I practice every chance I get. For instance, I make it my business to ride the elevator. This is the best way to keep track of who comes and goes. In our building everyone comes and goes by the elevators — except sometimes the people on the second floor use the fire stairs.

Two days ago at 8:15 A.M. I step into an Up elevator. I ride alone to the top floor — the 25th. I do not get off. The elevator goes down. It stops at nearly every floor. As usual at 8:15, the elevator is jammed by the time we reach the 17th floor. There is a lot of pushing and grunting. I think I will be crushed to death by this lady in front of me. But I do not say anything. Probably she is thinking she will be crushed by the man in front of her. Besides I think we will all die anyway from this other man's stinking cigar.

Finally the elevator reaches the lobby and everyone gets off. Everyone except me. Now is when I head back to 12H for breakfast. I make my move. As the lady in front of me gets off I step to the front of the elevator and press close to the wall where the self-service buttons are. I wait nervously for the doors to close. I do not like anyone to notice that I stay on the elevator. I do not want people getting wise to me.

The doors close. No one has seen me. I push the 12 button and get ready to relax. Then it happens. I get this feeling. I know that I am not alone. Slowly I turn my head to one side. I look out of the corner of one eye. I am right. I am not alone. There is a duck in the elevator with me. A white duck with orange feet.

Ducks are not allowed in our building. No Pets of Any Sort are allowed in the projects. So if anyone gets on this elevator now and sees me and this duck together, I am going to be in big trouble. It is not easy to get

into the projects—especially a low-income project like ours. The rent is low and they've got plenty of water and heat and all. You have to show need before you can even get on the waiting list. We waited two years before our number came up.

"Listen!" I say to the duck. "I am not going to get us kicked out of here for a duck."

I look away. If anybody does get onto the elevator, he will not see me paying any attention to any duck.

But the elevator goes straight to 12 without stopping. The door opens and I dash out. I am safe. I will go and have my breakfast in peace, and the elevator will carry the duck to some other floor.

And then what? Who will find that duck next? What if it's the Housing Inspector? What if it's somebody that likes to eat duck?

I turn around and look into the elevator. The duck is just standing there on these ridiculous orange feet— looking at me.

As the doors start to close, the dumb duck quacks. I can't stand it. I stick my arms through the closing doors just in time. The doors open. I grab the duck and charge down the hall. Ducks are not my usual line of work. But I don't have anything against them either. And I just don't like the idea of anyone cooking a duck that has looked me straight in the eye and quacked.

"O.K., Easter," I say, "I'll take your case."

2

WEBFOOTED FRIEND

I call him Easter because I figure he is probably some kid's leftover Easter present. Easter was a long time ago, but that's the only time we ever get ducks coming into our neighborhood. At Easter there are always a lot of guys around selling baby ducks and chicks and bunnies from the country.

It is almost September. Next week I will go back to school. I figure Easter the duck must be special if he has managed to stay alive in the city all the way from Easter to September.

Maybe one reason he is still alive is because he is good at keeping quiet. When I get into 12H I put him into the laundry hamper until I can have a talk with my mother. I peek through the air holes in the side of the hamper. The duck just sits there peeking back at me, not making any noise at all. Maybe he is stupid or maybe it's just that he isn't a quacker. My mother says that I am still waters that run deep. I guess she means I think a lot even though I don't say much. Maybe Easter is like that.

Probably Easter is still alive because somebody who really loves him has been taking good care of him. I think it is important to find that somebody.

I explain all this to my mother at breakfast. I tell her how Easter quacked me straight in the eye. But she does not like the idea of a duck in our apartment one bit.

"We waited two years to get into the projects," she says, "and now you bring home a duck. A duck! If the housing police catch us with a duck in our apartment, we will all be out on the street. No, Gilbert, I won't have it!"

I take my mother's hand and lead her into the bathroom. I lift up the lid of the hamper.

"Look, Mama," I say.

We both look. Easter is still sitting there — real quiet — on my striped pajamas. He tips his head to one side and looks up at Mama. Maybe this is the only way a duck can look up, but it is still a pretty cute thing to do.

Mama puts the lid back down on the hamper and steers me by the head back to the kitchen.

"If your father were here—" she says, and I know then that I'm home free. My father isn't here. He's in the merchant marines and he won't be home again until the end of next month.

Mama gives me three days to find Easter's owner. I tell her I think she is great. She is.

3

RUFFLED FEATHERS

After breakfast Mama and I move Easter into the bathtub. We do not know anything about ducks, but we give him some water and some rolled oats. He takes a little of both. Then he makes a mess in the bottom of the tub and starts cleaning himself with his bill. I guess he feels at home. While I am cleaning up the tub he comes over and pushes my arm. What do you know— he's even friendly!

I would like to stay and play with him, but three days is not very long and I better get busy. Easter pulls out one of his wing feathers. I pick it up and start thinking.

First I ask myself what are the facts. I am pretty sure Easter is a lost duck and not a ducknapped one. After all, nobody would go to all the trouble of stealing a duck and then leave it in the elevator.

No, I am pretty sure Easter just walked into that elevator himself. I also think he is a project duck. Even Easter could not have walked through our neighborhood and stayed alive. The dogs would have gotten him. Or the cats. Or the kids. So Easter must be a lost project duck, who happened to wander out of somebody's apartment and into the elevator. Maybe he was following his owner.

344

I also know that whoever lost Easter loves and misses him very much. Anyone who would dare to hide a duck in the projects would have to be either crazy or in love with the duck. I mean, who wants to get kicked out on account of a duck? This thought reminds me I better get busy.

The doorbell rings. I answer and it's—*bonk, bonk*—Dennis Herter. Dennis is always bouncing a basketball and sort of nodding his head.

"You want to shoot a few baskets, Gilbert?" he says.

"No, Dennis," I say. "I'd like to, but I can't today. I'm on a case."

"On a case, hmm?" says Dennis. "Sure, sure. Big detective."

He shuffles off down the hall, bouncing his ball. *Bonk, bonk, bonk.* Dennis always talks tough as though he couldn't care less. Actually we are very good friends.

It is nearly noon when I walk out of 12H. I am still carrying Easter's wing feather and I still do not have any idea of where to look for his owner. I cannot put a note on the bulletin board in the laundry room because nobody in the projects, including me, is going to admit to having anything to do with a duck. I also can't just go from door to door asking because you never know who is going to report you to the Housing Inspector. Besides there are too many apartments for me to check in three days.

At 12:15 I step into the Down elevator. This is what I always do at noon—just to see who comes and goes. Besides, since I haven't a better plan, I think it is best to start looking for Easter's owner at the scene of the crime—where I found him, I mean.

At this time of day the elevator is usually empty going down and full going up. Today is no different. It is on the way down that I get two ideas.

My first idea is that I will look for familiar faces from this morning's run. Easter did not ring for the elevator by himself, so he must have gotten on with somebody else. Maybe that somebody saw him get on? I am not too hopeful about this idea.

346

Then suddenly this really great idea pops into my head. It's about Easter's wing feather. I take off my belt and put it around my head. Then I stick the feather into the back of the belt. To most people I will just look like any other kid playing Indian brave. But to Easter's owner I hope I will look like somebody with one of Easter's feathers.

At lunchtime the Up elevator is full of people who have been grocery shopping or who only work half days. I do not see anyone from the 8:15 run. They are mostly nine-to-five workers who don't come home until around 6:00. Nobody pays any attention to me and my duck feather.

I spend most of the afternoon wandering around the building, hoping that the right person will see me in my duck feather and ask about Easter. At 3:35 P.M. I even try hitting my hand over my mouth and yelling "woo-woo-woo" at the top of my lungs in the laundry room. But all that happens is that a lady tells me, "Look, if you want to play, go out on the playground where you belong."

I follow the lady's suggestion and try my woo-woo-woo approach on the playground. This time I am noticed all right, but all that happens is some little children start yelling with me.

By this time I'm fairly discouraged, but I decide to go along with the game for a while. I think I'm too old to be playing silly games with a bunch of little children, but this is as good a way as any to advertise Easter's feather.

I am comfortably playing dead by the sandbox, thinking that it's too bad to outgrow such fun, when the worst happens. I hear this *bonk, bonk, bonk* sound next to my ear. I open my eyes and it's Dennis Herter standing over me, shaking his head.

"On a case?" he asks. "Too busy to shoot baskets? Too *young* is more like it."

"Really!" I say. "I'm working now. This is all part of my plan."

I can see he doesn't believe me, but I don't try to argue. I mean, what's the point?

At 5:00 P.M. I am still fooling around on the playground. About this time people start picking up the children from the Day Care Center. All these children whose parents both work go by on their way home. I think for a minute that this one sad-eyed little boy is watching me. Maybe he is looking at my duck feather? I go over to him hopefully, but he just runs along after his big sister.

It's about time for me to head back to the elevators. Pretty soon the nine-to-five workers will be coming home, including the ones that were with Easter and me in the elevator this morning.

This time I do not get on the elevator. There are two elevators. I do not want to be up in one while the somebody who got on with Easter this morning goes up in the other. I stay in the lobby until 6:30 P.M. I recognize five faces from this morning. This proves that all my detective practice is working. Of the five people I recognize, I manage to speak to four about Easter. Well, I don't exactly mention Easter. I just ask if they noticed anything unusual in the elevator this morning. Or if they lost anything. They didn't. At least the four people I speak to didn't.

By 6:30 the lobby is empty. A few people are still coming in, but I give up and decide to go home for supper. I push the button for the elevator. When it comes there is this same sad-eyed boy in it. I hold the door for him to get off, but he just stands there.

I say, "Don't you want to get off?"

But he keeps standing there. Well, I figure he is just a little boy who likes to ride elevators. I can understand that. I sort of like them myself. So I push the 12 button and head for home. All the way up this boy keeps looking at me. He doesn't say anything. Once he sort of

350

smiles, but mostly he just keeps looking at me out of the saddest eyes you ever saw. Even after I get off at 12 I keep seeing those sad eyes in my mind.

Nothing much more happens that day. I fool around with Easter in the bathroom, but I don't do any more detective work. It's not that I'm lazy. It's just that I don't have any more ideas. I have two more nights and two more days left to find Easter's owner. But I don't have any more ideas.

I ask my mother what will happen if I don't find his owner. She says we will have to take him to an animal shelter. I know what that means. The End. Nobody in this city is going to adopt a full-grown duck, so the shelter will put him to sleep. Forever.

4

DEAD DUCK?

Things go just as badly the next morning, and I am feeling cross and tired when I come home for lunch. I open the door and see my mother looking upset. In the living room are two men. One is a housing policeman. I can tell by his uniform. The other is the Housing Inspector. He is carrying a clipboard.

Now I know what is wrong with Mama. Once in a while the Housing Inspector goes through the apartments in the projects. He is supposed to make sure that everything is clean and that no rules are being broken. He checks that you don't have Pets of Any Sort. Anything

like that is called an Infraction of the Housing Regulations and you can get kicked out for it. And right now we have a white-feathered, orange-footed infraction named Easter in our bathtub!

"You don't mind if we just have a quick look around, do you?" the Housing Inspector is saying.

"Well," says Mama.

Mama keeps our apartment cleaner than anybody's, so the Housing Inspector does not look very hard. Just the same my heart is pounding like mad when he looks toward our bathroom. I mean, just suppose Easter decides to quack hello to *him!*

But good old Easter doesn't say anything. Pretty soon the Housing Inspector and the policeman go away.

I am in the middle of hugging Easter when Mama comes into the bathroom and starts giving me her mad look. Actually I know she isn't really mad.

"I'm sorry, Mama," I tell her.

She tells me she's sorry, too. She says she knows she gave me three days to find Easter's owner, but she has changed her mind. It is too dangerous to keep a duck around. She doesn't know what we would do if we got thrown out. Neither do I. She says if I don't find Easter's owner by tomorrow morning, we will have to take him to the animal shelter.

We sit on the edge of the bathtub together and watch Easter. When he walks, his orange feet make this ridiculous slapping sound on the bottom of the tub. He already seems like part of the family. Mama likes him, too. I can see that she feels terrible. I hug her.

"It's all right, Mama," I tell her. "I understand."

But I don't understand. I mean I don't see why it's anybody else's business if you want to have a duck in your apartment—or an anteater—or anything. Just so long as it's in *your* apartment and doesn't bother anyone else.

354

5

HATCHING A PLAN

I do not argue with Mama about the three days getting cut short. By now I think I am a lousy detective and I don't see what good an extra day will do anyway.

All afternoon I wear my feather around the project. Nobody notices me except Dennis Herter, who says, "Still playing kids' games, hmm? You are something else!"

I don't try to defend myself.

Evening comes and I still don't have any new ideas about how to find Easter's owner. Mama and I are really down at supper.

After supper I say that I think I will go and take my bath now. This is a mistake. Mama knows right away how awful I am feeling if I do such a weird thing as taking a bath without being told.

While I am in the bath Easter walks up and down the edge of the tub, slapping his feet. I invite him to come in for a swim, but this only seems to upset him. He walks back and forth, quacking and nodding his head up and down. Maybe it's just that he doesn't like warm water. Still I get the idea he sort of knows he's supposed to swim, but that he doesn't know how. If I could keep him, I would teach him to swim.

At bedtime it really hits me. Tomorrow morning it's The End for Easter. Here I am supposed to be some great detective and I haven't done anything. I figure the least I can do is to use my head a little.

On a real case, a robbery for example, I would try to think like a thief. But this is no robbery. It is not even a ducknapping. Easter is not stolen. Easter is lost. All right then, I will think like a duck and see where that gets me.

This is easier said than done. I do not know anything about ducks, and Easter is the only duck I know.

Then I remember from school that wild ducks migrate. They fly hundreds and hundreds of miles to the same place every winter. They can do that because they have an amazing sense of direction.

Easter is not a wild duck. Easter is a domesticated duck from a farm. And he is a city duck at that—a duck that probably doesn't even know how to swim. Even if domesticated ducks are supposed to have a good sense of direction like wild ducks, the chances are that Easter hasn't learned how to use his. But it's an idea. It's a long shot, but there isn't much time left. A long shot is better than no shot at all.

I do not tell Mama my plan because I do not want to get her hopes up for nothing. Also I do not want her to say no. I just kiss her goodnight. Then I go to the bathroom and say goodnight to Easter. I say it loud so Mama can hear. But then I whisper, "See you later," to Easter.

Before getting into bed I slip this old hand mirror into my bathrobe pocket. Then I take my ball of pieces of string down from the closet shelf. It is a good thing I save string because I am going to need it for my plan. I put the string under my pillow, set the alarm clock for 1:00 A.M., and climb into bed.

I am not at all sleepy, but that is all right because I still have a few details to think out. Basically, my plan is to see if Easter can find his own way home. I know this sounds crazy, but it is the only thing I can think of left to try.

At 11:00 Mama comes in and kisses me on the cheek. After that I fall asleep for a while. Then suddenly I wake up. I have trained myself to wake up when the alarm gives this little click just before it goes off. I push the button down just in time. I am wide awake and the alarm has not sounded.

I put on my slippers and my bathrobe. Then I take the string from under my pillow and go to the bathroom. I do not know if Easter has been asleep or not, but when I open the door his shiny little eyes are open. He looks wide awake. I think this is a good sign.

"Keep quiet," I tell him. I tiptoe to the front door carrying Easter and my ball of pieces of string. I take the apartment key from the magnetic hook on the door. Then I let myself out into the hall.

6
SITTING DUCKS

I have to admit that I am a little afraid. Partly it's that I have never been out this late before in my life. Partly it is because I do not know what in the world I will do if I meet someone. But it's a choice between this and The End. So I do not hesitate.

I go straight to the elevator and push the Up button. I stand with my back against the wall next to the elevator. The elevator comes and the doors open. I hold out my hand mirror and look at it to see into the elevator. Luckily it is empty. I step quickly inside and push 25.

At 25 we get off. I carry Easter to the end of the hall and push open the door to the fire stairs. There I put him down and tie the string to one of his orange legs.

My idea is to take him to each floor and see if he recognizes any apartment. I do not dare to take the elevator. Even in the middle of the night there are always people coming and going in our building. One of these people is the housing policeman, and I sure don't want to meet *him*—not in my pajamas in the middle of the night with a duck on a string! This is why I have decided to use the fire stairs. I will lead Easter down the stairs. I will open the door to each floor and see if he seems at home anywhere.

I unroll a lot of string and open the door to the 25th floor. Easter only tips his head to one side and looks up at me in that cute way of his. Either 25 is not where he lives or else he doesn't know how to use his sense of direction. I wish I knew which. It is a long way to the lobby.

But I am not going to give up yet. I start down the stairs toward the next floor. Easter follows. For a duck he is pretty good at going down stairs. His orange legs are not long enough to reach the steps one foot at a time. So he jumps with both feet at once and lands on each step with a loud double slap.

He does not show any interest in the 24th floor. Or in the next. Or in the next. On the way to 21 I get the idea that he is tired. I can tell because he keeps sitting down on about every third step. So from now on I carry him and only put him down when I open the door to each floor.

I begin to have serious doubts about my plan. I feel almost sure that we have already passed Easter's floor and that he just doesn't know how to use his sense of direction. It has taken at least 45 minutes to go six floors. There are still eighteen to go.

I am just thinking of quitting and going home myself when the door on 18 opens. I peek through the railing on 19 to see who it is. It is the housing policeman. He looks up and down the stairs and then goes back inside. He doesn't see me but I am very nervous

because I did not know before that the housing policeman checked the stairway. Next time he checks he
will probably catch me and Easter.

Just the same, I decide to go on. 18 is not Easter's
floor. Neither is 17. And neither is 16.

On the next floor I make a big decision. I am cold and I
am tired. I decide that if nothing happens by the time
we get to my floor—12—I will give up and go home.

Nothing happens on 15 or 14. By the time we reach
13, I have lost all hope. I am nearly in tears and I am
hugging Easter almost to death. All the same I put
him down on 13 and open the door.

What do you know about that! He walks right in. He is
walking straight down the hall of the 13th floor,
slapping his great big silly orange feet! As fast as
I can I unroll my ball of pieces of string.

Easter stops in front of 13B and quacks. 13B is way at the other end of the hall. I cannot be at all sure that this is where he lives, but at this point I have nothing to lose. Neither does Easter.

So I tiptoe down the hall and cut the string from Easter's leg. I ring the doorbell of 13B hard, three times. Then as fast as I can I run back to the stairway.

I peek through the window. Nothing happens. I am just about to give up hope when the door of 13B opens. I could faint when I see who is at the door! It is that quiet boy with the sad eyes that I've been seeing everywhere. Only now he is talking about a mile a minute. His eyes are sparkling like crazy and he is hugging Easter and sort of laughing and crying all at once.

"So long, Easter," I whisper. Then I rush down the stairs to the 12th floor and let myself into 12H. I think I must be really tired because for some reason I am crying, too.

7
JUST DUCKY

As usual at 8:15 A.M. I step into the Up elevator for my morning run. The elevator is empty going up and it is the same as always going down—the crowding, the pushing, the grunting. Today there is no man with a stinking cigar. There is this lady with garlic breath. I think garlic breath is worse than the cigar.

But I am feeling good. I am glad about Easter and I am glad to be back on the job. Maybe now I'll pick up a more routine case—a mugging or something. Today I feel I could handle anything. But maybe I'll just hunt up Dennis Herter and shoot a few baskets for a change.

Everyone except me gets off at the main floor. I step up out of sight by the self-service buttons as usual. No one sees me. The doors close and I head home for breakfast.

Then it happens. I get this feeling again. I know that I am not alone. Slowly I turn my head to one side and look out of the corner of my eye. I am right. I am not alone. Easter is in there with me.

I am boiling mad. I love Easter. I care about what happens to him. I have gone to a whole lot of trouble to get him back to his owner. It burns me up that that sad-eyed boy has let Easter get lost in the elevator again the very next day after he has come home.

I push the 13 button. The elevator stops at 12, but I do not get off. I get off at 13 and go straight to 13B and ring the buzzer. I keep ringing and ringing until this girl answers. I am just about to give her a piece of my mind when *she* begins giving *me* a piece of hers.

I am speechless at this. I stand there holding Easter while this girl actually bawls me out for bringing him home!

She speaks very rapidly. She tells me the duck has to go. She says it belongs to her little brother. He got it for Easter last spring when they were still living in a tenement.

She says they finally got a chance to move into the projects. They have only been in America a year. Her parents do not speak any English. They do not understand about No Pets of Any Sort in the lease. The Inspector tells them to get rid of the duck. But they do not understand. They do not get rid of the duck. So the Inspector makes it very clear. If the duck does not go, they will be thrown out.

Her little brother is very sad. He is shy. He does not speak any English. The duck is his only friend in America. He is heartbroken that he must send his duck away. He does not have any idea of how to find a new home for his duck. So he puts it on the elevator. He figures everyone rides the elevator. He hopes someone who will love the duck will take him home.

All this time I am listening. I am not angry any more, but this girl is still furious.

"Two days ago," she says, "he came home a little bit happy. He said this nice boy took his duck home. He is sad still, but he feels glad because his duck has a good home. And then you bring him back! Why? So this morning my little brother can cry some more and put his duck on the elevator again? What's the matter with you? You want to break a little boy's heart?"

What can I say? I say, "Please let me explain."

But she will not listen. She says she must take her little brother to the Day Care Center now. He is putting on his coat this very minute. She pushes me away from the door. She says to go away quickly because she does not want her little brother to see his duck again.

So I go. What else can I do? I hide Easter under my sweater and get onto the elevator. I push 12 and start trying to think up what I will tell Mama.

Then I get this idea. I think I am going to go crazy from having so many ideas.

Once again I do not get off at 12. I go all the way back to the main floor. I walk straight through the lobby and out the front door with Easter under my sweater. At this point I am so mad that I don't much care who sees me with Easter.

I walk around to the back of the building and push open the door marked Day Care Center. I walk into the office and say that I want to see the head teacher.

This lady behind the desk says she is the teacher and would I care to sit down. I shut the door and start sounding off. I am not much of a talker except when I am mad. Now I am plenty mad. I tell her the whole story.

By the time the girl from 13B gets to the Center with her little brother, everything is all set and I am waiting in the playroom with the teacher.

The teacher asks the girl to wait a minute. She sits down and looks at me in this kind of surprised way. When all the other children get there the teacher calls the sad-eyed boy to her side. She whispers to him and points at me. By the time she stops talking he is smiling and nodding like crazy.

She sends the boy over to me. I take Easter out from under my sweater and give him to the boy. Before I can stop him he gives me this huge wet kiss.

The teacher tells the rest of the class that Julio, the sad-eyed boy, is going to share his duck with all the children at the Day Care Center. Easter will be a Day Care duck and Julio will be in charge of him.

Pretty soon I leave. Julio is still smiling and trying to talk to the other children, who are all crowding around him. He is going to have lots of friends now, and Easter has a good safe home at last.

I am just heading back up to 12H for breakfast when this girl steps into the elevator with me. She is not angry any more. She is blushing.

"My name is Rita," she says. "I am sorry—"

"Skip it," I tell her. "It's O.K."

Letter Symbol for a Sound	Key Word and Its Respelling	Letter Symbol for a Sound	Key Word and Its Respelling
a	pat (PAT)	oo	boot, rule (ROOL)
ah	far (FAHR)	or	for (FOR)
ai	pain (PAIN)	ow	cow (COW)
aw	jaw (JAW)	u	put, book (BUK)
ay	pay (PAY)	uh	cut (KUHT)
e	pet (PET)	ch	church (CHERCH)
ee	bee (BEE)	hw	when (HWEN)
ehr	berry (BEHR -ee)	ks	mix (MIKS)
er	term (TERM)	kw	quick (KWIK)
i	pit (PIT)	ng	thing (THING)
igh	sigh (SIGH)		finger (FING -gər)
ihr	pier (PIHR)	sh	shoe (SHOO)
o	pot (POT)	ss	case (KAYSS)
oh	oh, boat (BOHT)	th	thing (THING)
oi	oil (OIL)	th	this (THIS)
		zh	pleasure (PLEZH -ər)

y used in place of (igh) before two consonant letters as in child (CHYLD)

ə represents the sound for any vowel spelling when a syllable is sounded very weakly, as in the first syllable of about, or the last syllables of item, gallop, or focus, or the middle syllable of charity.

Glossary

ab•a•cus (AB-ə-kəss) A counting tool made as a frame with rows of beads: An *abacus* can help you add and subtract.

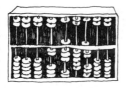

a•ban•don (ə-BAN-dən) To leave behind; to go away from. **abandoned, abandoning.**

a•ble–bod•ied (AY-bəl-bod-eed) Strong; healthy.

ache (AYK) 1. A dull, steady pain: I didn't sleep because of the *ache* in my tooth. 2. To have a dull, steady pain: John's stomach *aches* from all the candy and ice cream he ate. **ached, aching.**

ad•mi•ral (AD-mər-əl) A high officer in the Navy.

ad•mire (ad-MIGHR) To think highly of; to look upon with great liking and respect: I *admire* firemen for their courage. **admired, admiring.**

a•gen•cy (AY-jən-see) 1. A business that performs a service or acts in place of another business or person: I got a summer job through an employment *agency*. 2. A special government department.

am•ber•gris (AM-bər-griss) A gray, waxy material that comes from whales. It is used in making perfume.

an•cient (AYN-shənt) 1. Very old. 2. Belonging to times past.

Ar•a•bic nu•mer•als (A-rə-bik NOO-mər-əlz) The numbers 0, 1, 2, 3, 4, 5, 6, 7, 8, 9.

a•ston•ish•ment (ə-STON-ish-mənt) Surprise; amazement.

as•tron•o•mer (ə-STRON-ə-mər) A person who studies the sun, planets, and other bodies in the heavens.

a•wait (ə-WAYT) To wait for. **awaited, awaiting.**

bast A fiber from the inside bark of lime trees, used in making rope.

bawl 1. To shout or call loudly: The sergeant *bawled* the orders. 2. To cry out loud: The child *bawled.* **bawled, bawling.**

bear (BAIR) 1. To carry. 2. To produce, especially of plants: The trees *bore* fruit. **bore, borne, bearing.**

bid 1. To offer: Jim *bid* five dollars for the chair. 2. To order; command. **bade, bidden, bidding.**

birch (BERCH) A tree with smooth white bark and hard wood; the wood from this tree. **birches.**

boar (BOR) A wild hog or pig.

boast (BOHST) 1. What a person says when he brags. 2. To brag or speak too well of oneself. **boasted, boasting.**

bore (BOR) 1. To make tired and not interested: Long speeches *bore* me. 2. To make by drilling or digging: We will *bore* holes in the board for the screws. **bored, boring.**

brace (BRAYSS) 1. An object that holds something together or in place. 2. A device used to correct or support part of the body: Tony wears an ankle *brace* when he

plays basketball. 3. To support or hold up; strengthen. **braced, bracing.**

brah•man (BRAH-mən) In India, a member of the class of religious leaders.

brave (BRAYV) A warrior from an Indian tribe.

breech•es (BRICH-iz) Knee-length men's or boys' pants.

bril•liant (BRIL-yənt) 1. Shiny; very bright; sparkling. 2. Very smart.

buf•fa•lo (BUHF-ə-loh) A wild ox-like animal: In Asia, the water *buffalo* is trained to do work.

bur•den (BERD-n) 1. An unusually heavy load. 2. Anything that causes difficulty or hardship. 3. To load; load too heavily; weigh down with work, worry, duty, or sorrow.

bur•row (BER-oh) 1. A hole or tunnel in the ground, especially one an animal made to live in. 2. To dig a tunnel or hole in the ground. **burrowed, burrowing.**

caf•e•te•ri•a (kaf-ə-TIHR-ee-ə) An eating place in which customers select food at a counter and carry it to tables.

case (KAYSS) 1. A box; a container: My watch came in a plastic *case.* 2. A situation or condition. 3. An action of law: The judge heard the *case.* 4. A problem: The detective solved the murder *case.*

ca•the•dral (kə-THEE-drəl) 1. A large or an especially important church. 2. The main church under a bishop.

cau•tion (KAW-shən) 1. Carefulness: They approached the scene of the accident with *caution*. 2. A warning. 3. To warn. **cautioned, cautioning.**

ceil•ing (SEE-ling) The top surface of a room: Dad painted the walls blue and the *ceiling* white.

cel•lo•phane (SEL-ə-fayn) A thin clear paper used for wrapping.

cham•ber•lain (CHAYM-bər-lin) One who has control of running a palace; an aide to the king.

cho•rus (KOR-əss) 1. A group of singers. 2. The part of a song that is repeated after each stanza. 3. To say the same thing with everyone keeping together. **chorused, chorusing.**

churn (CHERN) To stir up; cause to tumble and foam. **churned, churning.**

ci•gar (si-GAHR) Shredded tobacco rolled in a tobacco leaf for smoking.

cloak (CLOHK) A loose piece of clothing or outer garment; like a cape.

clue (KLOO) Anything that helps to solve a mystery or a problem.

coarse (KORSS) 1. Rough; not smooth: Some overalls are made from *coarse* material. 2. Rude; not having good manners.

col•o•ny (KOL-ə-nee) 1. A group of people who settle a new area for their country. A *colony* of men and women landed at Plymouth Rock. 2. An area under the control of a foreign country: England's first *colony* in America was Virginia. **colonies.**

col•umn (KOL-əm) 1. A row of words, numbers, or other things: I added up a *column* of numbers. 2. A tall post that holds up part of a building. 3. A special section of a newspaper: Dad reads the sports *column*.

com•mer•cial (kə-MER-shəl) An advertisement on radio or television.

com•mu•ni•cate (kə-MYOO-nə-kayt) 1. To make (something) known, usually by telling or writing. 2. To share thoughts or feelings. **communicated, communicating.**

com•put•er (kəm-PYOO-tər) An electronic machine that can figure out difficult mathematical problems with great speed and can store, relate, and reproduce large amounts of information.

con•sult (kən-SUHLT) 1. To look up or ask for facts or advice: He did not know what the word meant, so he *consulted* the dictionary. 2. To discuss. **consulted, consulting.**

con•tin•ue (kən-TIN-yoo) To go on with; to keep going or moving: Did the players *continue* the game during the severe rainstorm? **continued, continuing.**

coun•cil•man (KOWN-səl-mən) A member or a group that gives advice to a leader or ruler.

cre•ate 1. To make: A good artist can *create* great pictures. 2. To be the cause of: Jack *creates* problems wherever he goes. **created, creating.**

crit•i•cize (KRIT-ə-sighz) 1. To judge or test. 2. To find fault with; blame. **criticized, criticizing.**

crop (KROP) A harvest; a farm product that is gathered at the end of a season: The farmer has a good corn *crop* this year.

crys•tal (KRISS-tl) 1. A very fine clear glass. 2. A kind of rock, usually shiny.

cur•tain (KERT-n) A cloth covering for a window, stage, or other opening.

daz•zle (DAZ-l) 1. To impress: The power of the huge waterfall *dazzled* us. 2. To overcome or confuse (usually by light): The firecrackers *dazzled* the children. **dazzled, dazzling.**

de•code (dee-KOHD) To change from a code into ordinary language. **decoded, decoding.**

de•sign (di-ZIGHN) 1. A plan for drawing used as a guide for making something. 2. A pattern or arrangement; a picture. 3. To make a design. **designed, designing.**

des•per•ate (DESS-pər-it) 1. Having a great need or desire: The hungry man was *desperate* for food. 2. Ready to run any risk.

des•tin•y (DESS-tə-nee) 1. Something that is sure to happen. 2. The force that seems to make things happen. **destinies.**

de•vel•op (di-VEL-əp) 1. To improve or build up. 2. To grow: A child *develops* quickly. **developed, developing.**

de•vour (di-VOWR) To eat up; to eat very fast. **devoured, devouring.**

di•al (DIGH-əl) 1. A flat, round device with numbers or letters on it, used to show information or to control something. 2. To use a dial, as on a telephone or TV set. **dialed, dialing.**

dis•be•lief (diss-bə-leef) A failure or refusal to believe.

dis•ease (di-ZEEZ) An illness; an unhealthy condition: Chicken pox is a *disease*.

dis•heart•en (diss-HAHRT-n) To discourage, take away hope: He *disheartened* us with the bad news. **disheartened, disheartening.**

doubt•ful (DOWT-fəl) Uncertain; not sure: It was very *doubtful* whether the team could win the game.

dump•ling (DUHMP-ling) 1. A small ball of bready dough cooked in and served with soup or stew. 2. A crust or pastry containing fruit.

dune (DOON) A hill of sand formed by the wind.

dun•geon (DUHN-jən) A dark jail or cell, usually underground.

dusk (DUHSK) The time of day when it's getting dark.

dye (DIGH) 1. Something used to color cloth or other materials: Easter egg *dye*. 2. To color something by using dye. **dyed, dyeing.**

ech•o (EK-oh) 1. To sound back: The cliff *echoed* Paul's voice. 2. To repeat or sound like. **echoed, echoing.**

el•der (EL-dər) 1. Older. 2. An older person.

em•blem (EM-bləm) A symbol or sign standing for an idea or a thing. The bald eagle is an *emblem* of the United States.

en•code (ən KOHD) To put something into a code or a system of secret signs or writing. **encoded, encoding.**

en•cy•clo•pe•di•a (en-sigh-clə-PEE-dee-ə) A book or set of books that gives many facts about many different things.

e•quip•ment (ih-KWIP-ment) Things that are needed in certain activities.

e•ven•tu•al•ly (ih-VEN-choo-ə-lee) Finally, at some time in the future.

ex•tend (ek-STEND) 1. To stretch out to full length: *Extend* your arms. 2. To spread out; reach: The ocean *extended* as far as we could see. **extended, extending.**

fast To go without food. **fasted, fasting.**

fier•y (FIGHR-ee) 1. Made of fire. 2. The color of fire: *fiery* red hair. 3. Easily excited: a *fiery* temper. 4. Very hot.

fife (FIGHF) 1. A long, thin musical instrument that is played by blowing in one end. 2. To play a fife. **fifed, fifing. —fifer.** One who plays a fife.

fig•ure (FIG-yər) 1. A shape: A circle is a *figure*. 2. A number that is not written in words: The number "12" is a *figure*. 3. To use arithmetic. 4. To reason or think out something. **figured, figuring.**

filch (FILCH) To steal, especially small amounts or things of little value. **filched, filching.**

flute (FLOOT) A long, thin musical instrument like a fife.

for•bid (fər-BID) To make a rule against; order not to (do something). **forbade, forbidden, forbidding.**

for•eign (FOR-in) 1. Away from one's homeland: They visited many *foreign* countries. 2. Of or from another country: She is learning a *foreign* language. 3. Out of place; not belonging: The diner found some *foreign* matter in his coffee.

fran•tic (FRAN-tik) Excited; wild with anger, pain, fear, sadness, or excitement.

fron•tier (fruhn-TIHR) 1. An area that is not fully explored: The settlers built a cabin on the *frontier.* 2. A border between countries.

fum•ble (FUHM-bəl) 1. To drop or knock over by accident. 2. To handle something clumsily.

fur•nish•ings (FER-nish-ingz) 1. The furniture, drapes, carpets, and other items in a room. 2. The clothing that people wear: The store has a sale on men's *furnishings.*

fu•ry (FYUR-ee) Extreme anger; rage. —**furious** (FYUR-ee-əss) Full of anger or rage.

fu•ture (FYOO-chər) The time to come; not the present or past.

gag 1. To put something over or in someone's mouth to keep the person from talking or shouting. 2. To choke on.

game•ly (GAYM-lee) 1. With courage. 2. In a good-natured way. 3. Willingly.

gape (GAYP) 1. To open the mouth wide. 2. To stare or look with the mouth open. 3. To become wide open. **gaped, gaping.**

gen•er•ous (JEN-ər-əss) 1. Unselfish; willing to give or share. 2. More than enough: She had a *generous* piece of pie.

glee•ful•ly (GLEE-fəl-lee) Happily; joyfully.

god•dess (GOD-iss) A woman god; a being thought to have special powers. **goddesses.**

gorge (GORJ) To eat fast and greedily. **gorged, gorging.**

gourd (GORD) A hard fruit with a thick shell that can be dried and then used as a cup or bowl.

grat•i•tude (GRAT-ə-tood) Thankfulness.

grave•ly (GRAYV-lee) In a serious or thoughtful way.

grief (GREEF) 1. Great sadness. 2. Any cause of sadness or suffering.

grim•ly (GRIM-lee) 1. Without giving up. 2. In a stern or harsh way.

grudg•ing•ly (GRUHJ-ing-lee) Without wanting to; unwillingly.

guide (GIGHD) To show the way or lead; to direct: The control tower *guided* the jet to a safe landing. **guided, guiding.**

gym•na•si•um (jim-NAY-zee-əm) A large room or building for sports and exercise.

half-mast (HAF-MAST) The middle of a flagpole or mast where a flag is flown as a signal of trouble or of sadness.

hard•ship (HAHRD-ship) Something that causes great difficulty or sadness.

har•mo•ny (HAHR-mə-nee) 1. State of getting along well. 2. Sounding or looking good together. **harmonies.**

has•ten (HAY-sən) To hurry. **hastened, hastening.**

hast•i•ly (HAYST-ə-lee) 1. Quickly; fast; hurriedly. 2. Carelessly.

he•ro (HIHR-oh) A person who is very brave or does many good things for others. **heroes.**

he•ro•ic (hih-ROH-ik) 1. Like a hero; brave; fearless. 2. Like what a hero does: It was a *heroic* rescue.

her•ring (HEHR-ing) A small fish, often eaten.

hoe (HOH) 1. A garden tool with a small blade and a long handle: A *hoe* is used for digging in soil. 2. To dig, break up, loosen soil, or weed with a hoe. **hoed, hoeing.**

ho•ly (HOH-lee) Having to do with religion.

hoop A circle or band of metal or other material.

ho•ri•zon (hə-RIGH-zn) The line where the earth and sky seem to meet.

hurl (HERL) To throw hard. **hurled, hurling.**

i•den•ti•fy (igh-DEN-tə-figh) 1. To tell or show who or what someone or something is. 2. To recognize. **identified, identifying.**

Ig•nore (Ig-NOR) To pay no attention to. **ignored, ignoring.**

im•pa•tient (im-PAY-shənt) Not able to wait; not patient. —**impatiently** In an impatient way.

in•de•pend•ence (in-di-PEN-denss) The ability to act without control by others; freedom.

jack•al (JAK-əl) A doglike wild animal.

jeal•ous (JEL-əss) Wanting what someone else has.

jour•ney (JER-nee) A trip from one place to another.

joy•ous•ly (JOI-əss-lee) Happily; gladly.

Lat•in (LAT-ən) A language used in Italy and most of Europe many years ago.

loft (LAWFT) 1. The upper floor of a barn where hay is stored. 2. The upper floor of a warehouse. 3. An attic.

lope (LOHP) To run with long strides. **loped, loping.**

lo•tus (LOH-təss) A water lily; a plant with large waxy blossoms. **lotuses.**

luck•i•ly (LUHK-i-lee) By good luck; not by planning or work.

lurk (LERK) To hide or wait, especially in order to attack. **lurked, lurking.**

ma•gi•cian (mə-JISH-ən) 1. A person, like a witch or a fairy in a story, who has mysterious powers. 2. A person who does puzzling tricks to entertain others.

mar•vel (MAHR-vəl) An amazing or wonderful thing.

mar•vel•ous (MAHR-vəl-əss) 1. Wonderful, unbelievable. 2. Of top quality; the best.

mas•ter•mind (MASS-tər-mighnd) The member of a group who plans an activity.

ma•te•ri•al (mə-TIHR-ee-əl) 1. The substance out of which a thing is made. 2. Cloth.

math•e•mat•ics (math-ə-MAT-iks) The study of numbers, measurements, and shapes.

men•tion (MEN-shən) To speak of or talk about briefly. **mentioned, mentioning.**

min•u•et (min-yoo-ET) A slow, formal dance.

mon•goose (MONG-goos) A small animal of Africa and Asia that looks like a weasel and hunts snakes. **mongooses.**

mush (MUHSH) 1. A food like oatmeal, but made from ground corn. 2. Anything thick and soft.

mus•ket (MUHSS-kit) A long gun, fired from the shoulder.

mut•ter (MUHT-ər) 1. To speak unclearly in a low voice. 2. To grumble or complain. **muttered, muttering.**

mu•tu•al (MYOO-choo-əl) 1. Shared in equal amounts: John and Henry had a *mutual* friendship. 2. Shared or taken part in by two or more.

mys•ter•y (MISS-tər-ee) 1. Something that is unknown, unexplained, or secret. 2. A book about a puzzling crime. **mysteries.**

na•tion (NAY-shən) A land or country and the people who live there: The United States is a *nation*.

na•tion•al (NASH-ən-əl) Having to do with a nation: The eagle is the *national* bird of the United States.

na•ture (NAY-chər) 1. The world, including all things not made by people. 2. The way a person, animal or thing almost always acts: It's a cat's *nature* to chase mice.

nav•i•gate (NAV-ə-gayt) 1. To direct where a ship or airplane goes. 2. To sail; travel in a ship. **navigated, navigating.**

no•tion (NOH-shən) 1. A general idea. 2. A view or theory.

nu•mer•al (NOO-mər-əl) A word, figure, or letter used to stand for a number: Two, 2, and II are *numerals*.

ob•ject (OB-jikt) 1. A thing that can be seen or touched. 2. The aim; the point or plan: The *object* of the game is to throw the ball into the basket. 3. (ob-JEKT) To refuse to agree; to be opposed to: Why do you *object* to my riding your bike? **objected, objecting.**

o•pin•ion (ə-PIN-yən) A thought that something is so or will be so: In my *opinion*, it will rain.

o•rig•i•nal (ə-RIJ-ən-l) 1. The first. 2. New; first of its kind. 3. The first form of something, one from which copies can be made.

o•ver•take (oh-vər-TAYK) To catch up with. **overtook, overtaken, overtaking.**

o•ver•whelm (oh-vər-HWELM) 1. To overcome or defeat completely. 2. To cover completely. **overwhelmed, overwhelming.**

pant 1. To breathe fast and heavily: The dog *panted* after his long run. 2. To speak with short, quick breaths. **panted, panting.**

par•a•keet (PA-rə-keet) A brightly colored bird that looks like a small parrot.

pas•sage (PASS-ij) 1. A corridor or hallway. 2. An opening in the body, as in nose or throat.

pa•tience (PAY-shənss) Ability to wait quietly; ability not to complain.

pa•tri•ot•ic (pay-tree-OT-ik) Loyal to and having love for one's country.

peer (PIHR) 1. To look at closely or intently. 2. To look through a small opening. **peered, peering.**

per•sist (pər-SIST) 1. To keep at, continue. 2. To last. **persisted, persisting.**

pew•ter (PYOO-tər) 1. A gray metal often used to make bowls and trays. 2. Things made of pewter.

phys•i•cal (FIZ-i-kəl) 1. Having to do with the body: The acrobats had great physical strength. 2. A health examination.

pi•pal (PEE-pəl) A kind of fig tree.

plan•et (PLAN-ət) A heavenly body like the earth, that moves around the sun.

plank (PLANGK) A long, thick wooden board.

plaque (PLAK) A flat piece of metal on a surface, like a monument, with words written on it, usually about someone or something important.

plea (PLEE) 1. A request; a call for help of some kind. 2. An excuse.

plod 1. To walk slowly and heavily. 2. To work steadily, but slowly. **plodded, plodding.**

por•ridge (POR-ij) Oatmeal or other cereal that is boiled and usually served with milk.

pounce (POWNSS) To jump or leap at, especially in order to catch. **pounced, pouncing.**

pre•cious (PRESH-əss) 1. Very valuable. 2. Beloved; very dear.

pri•vate (PRIGH-vit) 1. Secret. 2. Not public. **private eye** (Slang) A private detective; a detective who works independently or for an agency; not a police detective.

prop 1. Something put under or against an object to hold it up. 2. An object used in a play: The class collected all the *props* needed for the play. 3. To hold up with a prop. **propped, propping.**

prop•er•ty (PROP-ər-tee) 1. Something owned. 2. A piece of land that is owned. 3. A piece of furniture or any other thing that is used on a stage in a play; a prop. **properties.**

quan•ti•ty (KWON-tə-tee) An amount or number: Our family eats a large *quantity* of food. **quantities.**

ram 1. A male sheep. 2. A machine used to batter down walls. 3. To hit with force. **rammed, ramming.**

ra•vine (rə-VEEN) A deep, narrow cut in the earth.

re•al•ize (REE-ə-lighz) To understand. **realized, realizing.**

re•cord (REK-ərd) 1. A flat, circular object that gives off sound when it is played on a phonograph. 2. Written information about things that happen: We keep a daily *record* of the temperature. 3. The best that has been done in a contest, race, or other effort: The baseball player's six home runs were a *record* for the season. 4. The things known about someone or something: He had a good *record* in school.

re•fuge (REF-yooj) 1. A safe place: The climbers found *refuge* during the storm. 2. Safety or shelter. 3. A person that gives help.

rel•a•tive (REL-ə-tiv) A person of the same family.

res•tau•rant (RESS-tə-rənt) A place where people buy and eat meals.

re•sume (ri-ZOOM) To start again after stopping for a short while. **resumed, resuming.**

re•tort (ri-TORT) 1. A quick or clever answer. 2. To make a quick or clever answer. **retorted, retorting.**

re•veal (ri-VEEL) 1. To tell or make known. 2. To show.

ride (RIGHD) To be carried by an animal, a car, an airplane, or some other means of travel. **rode, ridden, riding.**

right•ful (RIGHT-fəl) Having a fair and lawful claim or right: the *rightful* owner.

sa•cred (SAYK-rid) Holy; set apart for religious purposes. 2. Deserving special honor.

scarce•ly (SKAIRSS-lee) Hardly, barely.

scroll (SKROHL) A long, rolled up paper that is written on; used mostly before books were printed.

seize (SEEZ) 1. To grab suddenly. 2. To capture. **seized, seizing.**

se•ri•ous (SIHR-ee-əss) 1. Thoughtful; solemn: a *serious* expression. 2. Important: Her first recital was a *serious* occasion.

sheer (SHIHR) 1. So thin it can be seen through: sheer cloth. 2. Very steep and high.

shep•herd (SHEP-ərd) 1. A person who guards and cares for sheep. 2. A person who guides and takes care of others. 3. German Shepherd or sheep dog.

shove (SHUHV) 1. To push roughly. 2. To move off or along by pushing. **shoved, shoving.**

so•cia•ble (SOH-shə-bəl) 1. Friendly; liking to be with people. 2. A friendly gathering; a party: We were invited to attend the yearly *sociable.*

so•lu•tion (sə-LOO-shən) 1. The answer (to a problem). 2. A mixture containing at least one liquid: a *solution* of salt and water.

soul (SOHL) 1. A person's deep inner self or feelings. 2. A person: Not a *soul* moved.

sprint To run at top speed, usually for a short distance. **sprinted, sprinting.**

spurt (SPERT) 1. To shoot out suddenly: a *spurt* of water. 2. To put out extra energy for a short while. **spurted, spurting.**

squat (SKWOT) To crouch; sit on one's heels with bent knees. **squatted, squatting.**

stalk (STAWK) 1. To follow quietly, especially in order to catch. 2. To walk in an angry or proud way. **stalked, stalking.**

sta•tion (STAY-shən) 1. The place where someone or something stands or is put. 2. To have (someone) stand at a certain place. **stationed, stationing.**

ster•e•o•scope (STEHR-ee-ə-skohp) An instrument with two eyeholes that makes pictures look three-dimensional.

strut (STRUHT) To walk in a proud way, as if showing off. **strutted, strutting.**

suc•ceed (sək-SEED) 1. To do or become or get something one wants. 2. To follow, come after. **succeeded, succeeding.**

suit (SOOT) 1. A set of clothes. 2. To be or make right for; to match. **suited, suiting.**

suit•or (SOO-tər) A man who wants a particular woman to marry him.

sus•pect (SUHSS-pekt) The person that seems to be guilty.

sword (SORD) A weapon with a long, sharp blade.

sym•bol (SIM-bəl) 1. A picture, sign, or object that stands for something else. 2. A letter or mark that stands for a word or idea.

sys•tem (SISS-təm) 1. An orderly or certain way of doing things. 2. A group of things or people that work together.

taunt (TAWNT) To make fun of; tease. **taunted, taunting.**

tem•ple (TEM-pəl) A building used for worshiping God or gods.

ter•ri•fy (TEHR-ə-figh) To frighten very much. **terrified, terrifying.**

the•a•ter (THEE-ə-tər) A building or place where plays or motion pictures are seen.

thrust (THRUHST) 1. To push or put out suddenly. 2. To make a quick, strong movement. **thrust, thrusting.**

tough (TUHF) 1. Hard to break, tear, or cut. 2. Rough; hard to handle. 3. Difficult; not easy.

tram•ple (TRAM-pəl) 1. To walk heavily on and crush. 2. To treat in a mean way. **trampled, trampling.**

trans•par•ent (transs-PAIR-ənt) 1. Easy to see through. 2. Clear; easy to see.

treas•ure (TREZH-ər) 1. Gold, jewels, or other valuable things that are saved or hidden away. 2. To love; care about very much. **treasured, treasuring.**

tre•men•dous (tri-MEN-dous) Very large or great; huge.

tri•an•gu•lar (trigh-ANG-gyə-lər) Shaped like a triangle, with three sides and three corners.

trib•ute (TRIB-yoot) 1. A deed or gift to show respect or gratitude. 2. Money or goods given to another for protection against harm.

troub•le (TRUHB-əl) A worry; a difficulty: Dad had *trouble* starting the car. 2. Hardship.

tur•quoise (TER-koiz or TER-kwoiz) 1. A valuable bluish-green stone. 2. A light bluish-green color.

un•cer•tain (uhn-SERT-n) 1. Not known. 2. Not sure.

un•for•tu•nate (uhn-FOR-chə-nit) 1. Unlucky. 2. Causing sadness or harm.

un•just (uhn-JUHST) Not fair.

up•ward (UHP-wərd) 1. Toward a higher place. 2. Toward a higher amount: Prices are moving *upward*.

vain (VAYN) 1. Conceited; proud of oneself. 2. Useless; worthless. **—in vain** Uselessly; with no result.

vast Very large in size, number, amount, or space.

ven•i•son (VEN-ə-sən) Meat from a deer.

vex (VEKS) 1. To annoy, bother. 2. To confuse. **vexed, vexing.**

vi•o•let (VIGH-ə-lit) 1. A small spring flower that may be purple, blue, white, or yellow. 2. A bluish purple color.

voy•age (VOI-ij) A long trip, especially by ship or boat.

wail (WAYL) 1. To cry or weep out loud. 2. To whine loudly. **wailed, wailing.**

war•y (WAIR-ee) Very careful and cautious.

weird (WIHRD) 1. Strange; frightening. 2. Odd; unusual.

wharf (HWORF) A platform near a shore that ships  can sail up to so they can be loaded or unloaded. **wharves.**

whim•per (HWIM-pər) 1. To cry softly; moan. 2. To whine. **whimpered, whimpering.**

wid•ow (WID-oh) A woman whose husband is dead.

wig•wam (WIG-wom) An Indian hut or tent made of animal skins over a framework of poles.

will (WIL) 1. The ability to make oneself do or not do something. 2. A great and strong desire: the *will* to win.

wor•ship (WER-ship) 1. To honor or adore. 2. To take part in a religious service.

wrath (RATH) Great anger or rage.

wring (RING) 1. To twist, rub, or squeeze. 2. To twist to get water out. **wrung, wringing.**

yon•der (YON-dər) Over there; in that direction.

yucca-leaf (YUHK-ə-leef) The leaf of a tropical plant with large, white flowers and long, pointed leaves.

ze•ro (ZIHR-oh) 1. The number or symbol 0. 2. Nothing. 3. Not any.